EXPLORA |

FROM ANGELS TO NEURONES

ART AND THE NEW SCIENCE OF DREAMING

J. Allan Hobson
and Hellmut Wohl

Mattioli 1885

FROM ANGELS TO NEURONES
ART AND THE NEW SCIENCE OF DREAMING

Authors:
J. ALLAN HOBSON
HELLMUT WOHL

ISBN 88-89397-13-6
2005, MATTIOLI 1885 SPA
WWW.MATTIOLI1885.COM

Design:
PAOLO CIONI

This special edition was supported
by an unrestricted grant
from Sepracor, Inc.
www.sepracor.com

J. ALLAN HOBSON AND HELLMUT WOHL > FROM ANGELS TO NEURONES

To Our Wives:
Lia Silvestri Hobson
and Alice Sedgwick Wohl

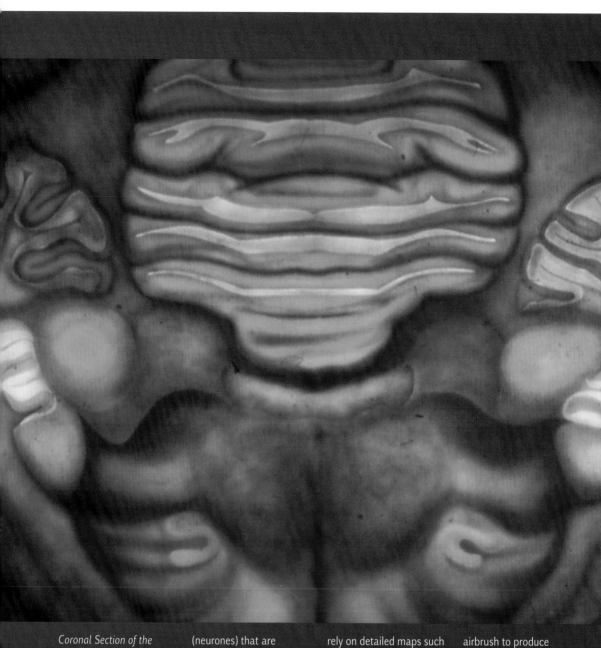

Coronal Section of the Pontine Brain Stem, painting by John Woolsey from a plate in Alvin Berman's Atlas of the Cat Brain Stem.

The control of the conscious states of waking and dreaming is effectuated by nerve cells (neurones) that are located in the brain stem. The brain stem connects the spinal cord to the upper brain where our awareness of the outside world (waking) and of our internally generated world (dreaming) take place. In order to study the brain stem precisely, scientists rely on detailed maps such as those produced by Alvin Berman. By day, John Woolsey, then an art student in Madison, Wisconsin, worked as Berman's research assistant. By night, Woolsey projected the brain slides on unsized canvas and used acrylic airbrush to produce colored images such as the one shown here. Little did young Woolsey know that his artistic creation represented the structural basis of dream consciousness.

FOREWORD

As if by dream-like chance, Allan Hobson and Hellmut Wohl met at a luncheon at Boston University in 1997 celebrating the two day conference on Dreaming in which they both had been invited to speak. It wasn't long before they agreed to write a book. But this book was a long time in the making. And their meeting, which was due, in part, to chance, was also very meaningful to both of them.

For many years before that meeting, Allan Hobson had been collecting art images representing sleep and dreams with a view to writing a book. He had even gone so far as to produce an elaborate proposal, called *Sleeping Beauty*, that showcased his essay on William Blake and Henry Fuseli entitled "Strange Bedfellows". But he was aware of his limitations in the field of art history and the project languished.

Enter Hellmut Wohl, the art historian whose interests in the Renaissance and Modern periods had already brought him to a consideration of dream art. His formalist analytic approach to art and his native engineering instincts made him an ideal partner for Allan Hobson, a psychiatrist/neurophysiologist whose violin d'Ingres had always been art history. Hellmut Wohl quickly realized the problems with Freudian dream theory and with the psychoanalytic study of art as well as appreciating the importance of neurophysiology in understanding the autocreativity of the human brain.

Our work together has been a genuine and mutually satisfying collaboration from start to finish. We agreed early on to concentrate on works of art, including film, roughly up to and not beyond the discovery of REM sleep in 1953. Although the past fifty years have seen a notable production of dream art in a variety of media, inclusion of this material would not have contributed significantly to our aim of demonstrating the consilience of art and science.

Writing the book was very significantly helped by our month-long stay at the Rockefeller Study Center in Bellagio, Italy during the early fall of the year 2000. By sharing a studio and a computer, and working all day including weekends, we were able to complete a first draft of the manuscript. Our wives were patient allies in this important process. We are grateful to the Rockefeller Foundation for this unique opportunity.

The technical assistance of Nick Tranquillo and Robert Gifford (in Boston), Luca Di Perri (in Messina) and Natalie Cerioli (in Parma) is gratefully recognised.

The evolution of the text over the subsequent years has been helped by Caroline Jones, several anonymous reviewers and such editors as Eve Sinaiko (at Abrams) and Nancy Grubb (at Princeton). We are happy that Paolo and Federico Cioni of Mattioli 1885 have chosen to publish the book. For us to realize its full visual possibilities is a dream come true. It is particularly appropriate that the book will have both an English and an Italian edition because Allan Hobson has decided to spend half his time in Messina, Sicily and Hellmut Wohl does research every summer at Villa I Tatti, the Harvard University Center for Italian Renaissance Studies in Florence.

Our respective universities have been sustaining and many outside agencies, including the National Institutes of Health and the MacArthur Foundation have supported the research that we report.

We understand that our book is challenging to the paradigms that most readers will bring to it. Our fond hope is that the marriage of art and science that we espouse will be clear, acceptable, and even transformative for those who read our text as well as admire the science and art images that illustrate it. The underlying issue of our book is nothing less than the mind-brain problem whose solution will go a long way to unifying the two cultures.

J. Allan Hobson
Hellmut Wohl

Table of Contents

Hieronymus Bosch, (detail), right-hand panel of the triptych The Garden of Earthly Delights, 1503-

1504, Museo del Prado, Madrid.

In the middle of Bosch's hallucinatory vision of hell is the image of the Egg Man, for which the

drawing of the Tree Man (shown on page 19) is a preparatory study.

Mere Productions of the Brain

Formal Aspects of the Dream State and the Imagery of Art

Those dreams that on the silent night intrude,
And with false flitting shapes our minds delude,
Jove never sends us downward from the skies,
Nor can they from infernal mansions rise;
But all are mere productions of the brain,
And fools consult interpreters in vain.

Jonathan Swift, *On Dreams, 1727*

The Christian angel is only one of a long line of ephemeral agencies given the responsibility of accounting for the wondrous nocturnal visions that are our dreams. Angels are the descendants of pagan winged gods, bearers of Swift's "false flitting shapes." During the past two millennia many Western dreamers and thinkers have attributed the oneiric experiences to winged messengers from beyond because they were ignorant of the auto-creative mechanisms within their own heads.

Now, at the beginning of the third Christian millennium, we are realizing that dreaming is a state of consciousness whose unique features and whose very existence are both engendered by physical and chemical changes in the brain that modern neuroscience has begun to specify. Although far from complete, this paradigm shift - from spiritual angel to physical neurone as the principle agent of dreaming - has far-reaching implications for the humanities in general and for theories of the making and viewing of art in particular.

The Angel to Neurone paradigm shift which we will develop in this book, was envisaged a century ago by Sigmund Freud. Freud's influence upon our thinking about the making and viewing of art has been profound. To Freud we owe our sensitization to the impact of many individual biographical and collective cultural forces that help to shape works of art and determine their content. But to the extent that Freud's aesthetic theory was formulated in absence of specific neurophysiological detail, it is in need not only of amendment but also of reformulation.

Freud believed that the adult yearns unconsciously to return to the lost world of childhood. One way in which this yearning is expressed is in dreams, another through art. According to Freud artists have the unique gift of remaining in touch with their earliest life experiences and of embodying these in their work; and creative inspiration depends on the artists' ability to tap the lost images, feelings, and longings of their childhood past.

We will suggest that Freud's views have unwittingly perpetuated aspects of the angel-agency, such as pre-ordination, prophecy, and interpretation, that they were designed to replace. We will further suggest that Freudian psychoanalysis, which regards mental products, including works of art, as compromises between biologically imperative drives and socially conditioned prohibitions, is scientifically questionable. In a similar way that medieval scholasticism led to centuries of textual exegesis and decoding of symbols, modern psychoanalysis has committed huge segments of academic and popular thinking to an effort to reduce creativity to a rehearsal of psychopathological conflict.

In this book we will propose that the auto-activating, chaotically open system of the dreaming brain provides the basis for bringing art and science together in a new, liberating synthesis. One of our goals will therefore be to suggest that the neurophysiology of dreaming offers a new insight into creativity and the creative process by accepting a commitment to unpredictability. Our position and its critique of psychoanalysis may be illustrated by Paul Delvaux's painting *L'École des Savants*. Delvaux and the Surrealists were committed to

Paul Delvaux, L'Ecole des Savants, 1958, Liechtenstein Museum, Vienna.

Delvaux, like other Surrealists, was interested not in the scientific investigation or psychoanalytic interpretation of dreams, but in dreams as a source of artistic inspiration. In Delvaux's painting a psychoanalyst interviews a patient (right), and a neurobiologist examines a brain (left). Neither looks at the dream scenario combining a deserted open space, railroad trains, and street lights in the center. We agree with Delvaux and attempt to explain our own approach to dream form in this chapter.

exploring the creative unpredictability of the dreaming brain as a source of artistic inspiration and to depicting it, as Delvaux has in the dream landscape in the center of his painting of which both the psychoanalyst talking to the live dreamer at the right and of the neurobiologist* who examines a dead brain at the left are unaware.

Universality of Dreaming

Because dreaming is an intrinsically creative act, every man can be said to be an artist while dreaming. We will describe how visual imagery of arresting clarity arises spontaneously in the brain during sleep, how emotions ranging from ecstatic elation to dread panic are simultaneously generated, and how visual imagery and feelings in dreaming are effortlessly and seamlessly integrated. At the heart of our model is the internal generation of percepts and emotions. In formulating our new theory we will seek to transcend the external agency, or angelic paradigm, and to cast doubt upon the commitment to interpretaility in so far as it is based on the erroneous view of the brain as a closed system. At the same time we will suggest that all effective and affecting art is dreamlike in so far as at it deals with the seamless integration of percept and emotion.

The brain-based theory of dreams that we will develop in this book is grounded in a formal analysis of dreaming as a creative process. As such, the brain-based science of dreams provides a means of examining imagination at its root. By viewing dreaming as the brain/mind's effort to create rather than to disguise meaning, as Freud thought, the new theory liberates both the art historian and the dreamer from the spell of psychobiography. This reversal of emphasis is also temporal.

Dreaming is more than a rehearsal of the past. It is also a harbinger of the future: not a prophecy to live out a particular fate, but an exhortation to recognize and to express our intrinsic creativity.

In our view, dreaming is as transparent, as rich, and as fundamentally unanalyzable as are works of art. We hope to show that far more can be learned from both dreams and art if they are regarded as sources of inspiration and enlightenment rather than as cryptograms concealing forbidden instinctual motives. Our discussion will be focused on works of art which were either inspired by dreams, or which are informed by a visual analysis of the processes characteristic of dreaming. Our position reflects that of Paul Klee expressed in a lecture he gave in 1924 on the sources and the process of artistic creation:

Artists with a real vocation are those who travel to within a fair distance of that secret cavern where the central organ of all temporal and spatial movement - we may call it the brain or the heart of creation - makes everything happen. Whatever emerges from this activity, call it what you will, dream, ideas, fantasy, should be taken seriously if it combines with the pictorial elements and is given form. Then curiosities become realities, realities of art, which add something more to life than it usually seems to have. For then we no longer have things seen and reproduced with more or less display of temperament, but we have visionary experiences made visible.

Art History Reconstructed

Brain-based dream science provides us with a framework for an illuminating journey

---

*The neurobiologist is Professor Lindenbrock, inspired by or copied from an engraving by Edouard Rion illustrating the Hertzel edition, published in 1864, of Jules Vern's *Voyage au centre de la terre*.

through the history of art and ideas. Recognizing that many artists and thinkers have perceived truths about dreams without being able to explain them, we will attempt to shed new light on our art-historical heritage by re-examining selected works of art through the lens of brain science. At the same time, we will suggest that artists who represented sleep and dreaming, whether directly or indirectly, intuitively grasped the formal identity between dreaming and art.

In this chapter we endeavor to make clear exactly what we mean by formal identity: We begin by a disclaimer. We do not mean substantive or ontological identity. We are not saying that dreaming and art are identical processes, but, rather, that they are processes with many shared formal features. We are not saying that every dreamer is an artist (or even that every artist is a dreamer), but that in dreaming, as in waking, we undergo a shift in mental state with specifiable formal features.

A work of visual art may be defined as an object which can directly evoke percepts and feelings in the viewer without the medium of language. While artistic experience is a universal human attribute, artistic talent is the ability to give form to experience in a way that evokes visual percepts and associated emotions in the viewer. Dreams, too, are sets of perceptions and related emotions which arise directly in the mind without the medium of language. Like works of art, dreams may have a narrative or metaphorical character which depends on language, but both are experienced primarily as vision and emotion, and both integrate vision and emotion in compelling, surprising, and meaningful ways.

THE RELEVANCE OF DREAM FORM AND DREAM CONTENT TO ART

We are fully aware of the intrinsically narrative character of human conscious experience, and of the fact that the search for meaning inevitably involves an effort to translate perception and emotion into the language of thought. Equally inevitable is the recourse in dream science to the dream report, since at the present state of neurophysiology the dream experience cannot be directly accessed by any third party observer. We also recognize that art history inevitably involves the interpretation of iconography. However, we see many dangers as well as limitations in this approach. We are not alone, for example, in questioning Freud's interpretation of the wolves in a purported drawing by a patient he called the Wolf Man as a symbolic representation of that patient's witnessing parental intercourse a tergo.

We want to make clear that by a formal approach to dreams and art we do not seek to explain - or explain away - the content and personal values of either dreams or works of art. It is our purpose, rather, to provide a foundation for approaching content with a scientifically based schema for understanding the process of dreaming and, by extension, of art-making. By dream form we mean the universal features of dreams, regardless of their content, specifically

(1) internally generated percepts, primarily visual but also motoric (akin to hallucinations) that are

(2) accepted as real (akin to delusions) despite being

(3) distinctively bizarre, discontinuous and incongruous (akin to orientational instability), all of which are associated with

(4) strong emotion (especially anxiety and fear but also elation and anger), most of which are

(5) completely forgotten or, at best, difficult to remember (akin to amnesia) unless keen attention is paid to the dream immediately upon awakening.

In short, by formal, we mean the mental, visual, and emotional characteristics of the

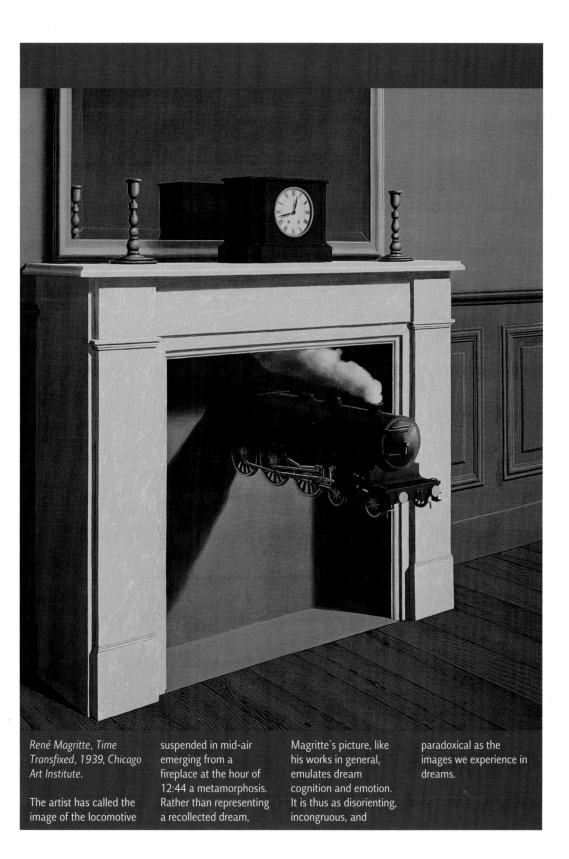

René Magritte, Time Transfixed, 1939, Chicago Art Institute.

The artist has called the image of the locomotive suspended in mid-air emerging from a fireplace at the hour of 12:44 a metamorphosis. Rather than representing a recollected dream, Magritte's picture, like his works in general, emulates dream cognition and emotion. It is thus as disorienting, incongruous, and paradoxical as the images we experience in dreams.

conscious experience of all persons, in whatever culture or period in history, and no matter what their specific content. The evidence of neurophysiology strongly suggests that dream form is ontologically primary to dream content, and that any approach to dream content which either ignores dream form or attempts to explain dream form by the analysis of content is putting the cart before the horse. To be sure, not all of the formal features of dreaming apply to art. Most works of art do not cause us to hallucinate, nor do they delude us into believing that they are real. By the same token, although works of art may be cognitively bizarre or disturbing, they may also evoke calm, peaceful, and reflective emotions. The reason for this is that artists work in waking, and we in turn behold their works in waking, a state of consciousness in which the formal characteristics of dream features are actively held in abeyance.

Whatever emotions are evoked by a work of art, they must be so seamlessly integrated with its content as to render the work's content as plausible and compelling as our dreams; and the capacity of a work of art to engage the viewers' perceptions is enhanced by its capacity to engage the viewers' feelings. The meaning of both works of art and of dreams stems from this integration of perception and emotion. Both perception and emotion are, of course, connected to content; and they are facilitated by certain contents more than others, as the enduring power of the work of Hieronymus Bosch shows us particularly clearly.

Bosch's Fantastic Landscape: Hallucination as a Natural State of Mind in Dreams and Art

Bosch's drawing traditionally called the *Tree Man* is a study for the so-called "Egg Man" in the Hell panel of the triptych of *The Garden of Earthly Delights* in the Prado. The drawing is a veritable primer in the distinctive formal aspects of dreams. The visual verisimilitude of the physically impossible humanoid tree that occupies the center of the picture is incongruously yet seamlessly integrated within a realistically depicted landscape. It is this rendering of the fantastic as springing directly from the natural - and as inextricably bound up with it - that gives the image its dreamlike conviction.

In the light of day - in the light of waking - there is no doubt in our minds that we are looking at a visual representation of an entirely imaginary, monstrous object. But Bosch nonetheless convinces us of the naturalness of his vision, and this normalization of the hallucinatory image, like the naturalization of the hallucinatory power of dreams is crucial to its success.

Rather than probe the mysterious object for its allegorical significance, we accept it as a natural product of the mind simulating an altered state of consciousness. In the same vein, we eschew the reduction of dream phantasmagoria to the symbolic transformation of instinctual forces that may have contributed to their genesis. The psychiatric label hallucination to describe dream vision may seem inappropriate because it tends to pathologize a state that is both normal and natural. Without dreaming sleep animals perish. And when dreaming sleep is curtailed, humans cannot learn simple tasks. We therefore need to explain why we use a word which denotes psychosis - the most extreme form of psychopathology - to describe a process which is essential to health. In doing so we wish to make the point that phantasmagoric artists like Bosch are as essential to the health of society as are dreams to the health of individuals.

In our view, the universal experience of hallucinatory dream vision shows us that psychosis is a natural - and in some circum-

Hieronymus Bosch, The Tree Man, c. 1503, Albertina, Vienna.

Bosch's drawing, a preparatory sketch for the Egg Man in the Hell panel of the triptych *The Garden of Earthly Delights*, resembles a dream image in its fluid instability, and in the believability, or normalization, of a seemingly impossible hallucinatory vision.

stances even a normal - state of mind. In our dreams we are all capable of generating fantastic landscapes, even though these rarely attain the comic grotesque character of Bosch's *Tree Man*. As we will try to show in the following chapter, the capacity to have fully formed, vivid, hyper-real (or surreal) visual hallucinations in sleep is a natural talent of every person. Bosch had the astonishing ability to embody this entirely natural process in works of art.

To our main point - that Bosch's *Tree Man* is dreamlike in its capacity to normalize or naturalize its seemingly impossible vision - we want to add two important caveats: first, the formal caveat that dreaming and the drawing by Bosch are similarly - but not identically - hallucinatory; second, that the content of our dreams and of Bosch's drawing may not even be similar. Our dreams do not as a rule include monsters, or mythological chimeras, or even cutaway persons with egg-like torsos.

Mental content of whatever form is always local, personal, and topical. Its metaphorical character is accordingly limited. But the media of its expression are universal. Contrastingly, our dreams consist of a seamless blend of the possible - even the banal - with the highly improbable and frankly impossible. And they are always uneasily poised on the edge of discomfort, and of an anxiety which may devolve into the horrific and the unbearably painful terror of nightmares. Our bodies may reveal their intrinsic decadence as when our teeth fall out, we feel paralyzed, or our limbs are hacked off in nightmarish dreams. And, most important for the formalistic argument, our dream characters are often chimeras, even if they are not mythological ones.

SEEING IS BELIEVING: THE DELUSIONAL ACCEPTANCE OF VISUAL IMAGERY

Telling a psychotic patient that the accusing voice that is heard or the fantastic insect that is seen crawling up the wall of his room are not real at all, but merely symptoms of his illness, is every bit as much a fool's errand as trying to convince ourselves during our dreams that we are not really awake but only experiencing the symptoms of sleep. Delusion goes hand in hand with hallucination precisely because there is no more convincing subjective experience than vivid perception. In our dreams we believe, indeed, we cannot but believe what we see and hear.

The fluid instability of dreams which compels our fearful belief is simulated by the incredibility of the balancing act of Bosch's *Tree Man*. Imagine that your feet are in boat-like shoes floating on the surface of water. We may have had dreams of skimming and staying both upright and afloat on oneiric ponds, canals, and rivers, but never when asked to balance on our heads a flat disk which holds a tall pitcher into which is stuck a tall ladder at half of whose height is a man pulling on a cable attached to a flag pole stuck into our cracked-egg ventrum.

All of this dream-like vertigo is being watched by a wise owl perched on a branch that soars as high as the ladder, as far above our head as our head is above the water. This suspended animation - an imbalance that is about to disequilibrate - is, as it were, a visual description of the hallucination-delusion process that takes over our brain-minds when we dream. The dynamic tension of the *Tree Man* appears to exist on the brink of disaster: certainly the tiny threads connecting the perilous ladder to the flag pole and the prows of the boat-shoes to the tree's knees cannot be expected to hold; but they do, and the whole illusion is held aloft, like a high wire act in the circus.

d his Cat Sleeping ... by the photographic studies of Theodore Spagna. Having acquired a time-lapse camera at an auction, Spagna portrayed the dynamics of sleep behaviour and revealed what he called "a hidden landscape" of postural sequences that were programmed by the brain's NREM-REM cycle mechanisms.

Both humans and their natural bed partne... animals tend to ch... their body position whenever the brai... changes its state.

sical beauty and ...nctive positions of ...sleep were ...d for the first time

Discontinuity and Incongruity: The Fracture Lines of Dream Cognition

Bosch's fantastic monster lives in a tranquil, routinely normal world, a device which further enhances the naturalization of the outlandish. The convincing form of Bosch's phantasmagoric visions is as much a part of nature as the conventional landscape with its trees, birds, animals, and church spires which compose the screen upon which his bizarre vision is projected. In waking a tree is just a tree. We have to squint and let our minds fall into the twilight zone to see it as a person. Yet all trees do have trunks (torsos) and roots (limbs) which can become the building blocks of anthropomorphic transformation. In dream generation and in phantasmagoric art, the associative rules that govern such transformations are loosened with the result that the continuity between persons, times, places, and actions is ruptured and the contextual wholeness of dream scenes is fragmented.

Rarely is the discontinuity and incongruity in our dreams as abrupt and as fractious as in Bosch's drawing. But it is always there. When we analyze dream reports of our experimental subjects on a line by line basis, we see this every line. It may be microscopic - and subtle - or it may be dramatic and obvious. Bizarreness, discontinuity, and incongruity are at the very heart of what we mean when we say "I had the strangest dream"; and of what Bottom in *A Midsummer Night's Dream* means when he says:

I have had a dream past the wit of man to say what dream it was...The eye of men hath not heard, the ear of men hath not seen. Man's hand is not able to taste, his tongue to conceive. Nor his heart to report what my dream was.

In a sense, we might suppose that this strangeness goes hand in hand with hallucination and delusion. While these two processes do conspire together, dream bizarreness reflects much more than the ability to visualize and believe visions to be real. Indeed, it places an added burden on the self-reflective awareness of the dreamer, just as Bosch's fantastic creature puts a greater demand on our suspension of disbelief than, for example, Pieter Brueghel's equally convincing depictions of Flemish everyday life. In both cases, the painting is dazzling in its simulation of natural reality; but in Bosch's hands, we are asked to go a step further.

Reading Bosch's drawing from the bottom up, consider the following examples:

Boat Shoes: The Tree Man's shoes are boats. Being made of wood, they are credibly buoyant. But boats are not shoes, and they could neither possibly support the weight of the Tree Man nor maintain the stability of the elaborate structure poised anxiously above them.

Branch-Limbs: At once fore-limbs and hind-limbs, the tree trunk legs enhance our sense of bizarreness by reducing Bosch's monster with its human head to something closer to a monkey or even, as in Kafka's Metamorphosis, to a giant beetle. The simian allusion is conveyed by the fact that the Tree Man is, as it were, walking on his knuckles, and the evocation of a giant beetle is supported by the egg-like torso. The metamorphosis is further advanced by having the smaller branches of the trunk-limbs actually pierce and pass through the torso-ventrum.

Trunk-Torso: The visual center of the picture and the backward and downward pulling vector that threatens to undo the delicate balance is the creature's belly-rump. This incongruous anatomical element is radically discontinuous. The gaping hole in its side reveals its gluttonous function. Feeding is directly and transparently represented by the banquet table with its diminutive diners, real little men, inside the gigantic imaginary *Tree Man*.

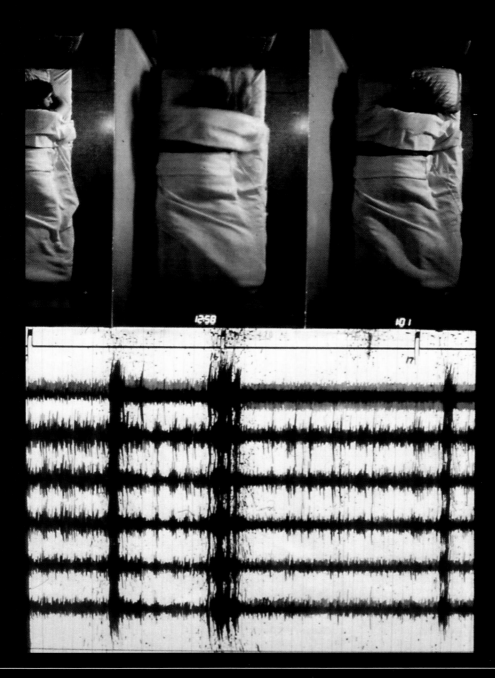

The Sleeping Brain and Body.

Despite the availability of time-lapse photographic techniques of Edward Muybridge and Jules-Etienne Marey, who worked in Freud's time at the end of the 19th century, it was almost a century before sleep was the subject of photographic study by the late Theodore Spagna. Spagna's work spanned a wide variety of human and animal subjects sleep in natural, captive, and laboratory settings and revealed a clear pattern of posture shifts which were the behavioral read outs of the internal and automatic changes in brain state that underlie the NREM-REM cycle. We show one such posture shift here.

The little men in the boat, in the pitcher, and on the ladder play the same role. They reframe and anchor the fantastic in the ordinary. At the same time they ironically convey the sense of overall incongruity because, like the blind man describing the elephant, none of them can perceive the whole, the grand design. They are thus doomed, like Gulliver's Lilliputians, to struggle in vain to harness forces that are beyond them. Their paltry integrative efforts are futile, as the whole edifice of human ambition is about to fall apart.

The root of dream bizarreness is the cognitive disequilibrium caused by orientational instability. Times, places, persons, and actions change without notice. At one moment we may be walking - or running - in a sylvan landscape. At the next moment we find ourselves inexplicably seated at a dining table, entirely unaware of the impossibility - except in imagination - of such a scene shift. We do not ask ourselves any more than we ask Bosch how these things could happen. In this book, we will suggest answers to this question. One is that emotion provides the integration that orientation has betrayed. The other is that working memory, which is essential to orientation, has ceded pride of place - in the brain as well as in the mind - to emotion. Bosch gleaned these truths half a millennium before neuroscience demonstrated them.

Head-Tray-Pitcher-Ladder

To make the monkey-beetle torso credible, Bosch has tacked an out-of-scale head on its front end, once more breaking the anthropomorphic mold: The Tree Man has become a Man Tree. The head is too small and inadequate for its usual task: to comprehend, to integrate, and to command. The head-end, Bosch seems to be saying, cannot balance the tail-end. Reason cannot manage the vegetative part of us because our appetites are too strong. The impish smirk on the face is at once provocative and self-effacing. Look at me, it says, am I not as ridiculous as I am marvelous?

In dreams, the same sort of failure to manage our vegetative selves depends upon a diminution in the power of reason because of the impairment of working memory. And in dreams we experience chimeras that are every bit as impossible as the oneiric characters that change their identity or assume aspects of several persons known to us and unknown. Our studies of the limits of this sort of metamorphosis, however, show that in dreams it does not usually extend across such barriers as plant-human that the Bosch image so whimsically poses.

To emphasize the hopeless ambition of the cerebral balancing act that is our major challenge as humans, Bosch piles the tray, the pitcher, and the ladder on top of the Tree Man's head. While these objects may be heavy enough to counterbalance the overhanging viscera in the monster's anal cavity, they do not make its appetites less unruly. Household utensils (the pitcher) and architectural tools (the ladder) are admirable inventions, but they may only make the integrative task more difficult, especially if they are used for perverse goals. The head pitcher is ten to twenty times larger than the belly pitcher, and its use is more ambiguous. It contains not ale but more little men, homunculi who fish in the air for unforthcoming answers to imponderable questions.

Blinded by our involvement in the topical, the local, and the trivial, we aspire to get up and have a look around. By climbing a ladder, one of Bosch's little men is, like us, trying to escape from the ignominy of dream enchantment. By using a psychological ladder, we can sometimes successfully acquire enough waking reason to know that we are dreaming, and to try to do something about it, to become what we call lucid, enlightened, or insightful.

July 16 - 17.

Desiring a dreamless night I drank a glass of brandy, and then took an amytal tablet. One I dream as follows:— Sperry (or just possibly Oman) & I were playing golf. ... was on one side of road, and a dense forest of trees on the other. Drove off into trees. All my shots were poorly hit — one striking a tree, while another flew into a small, pen enclosed by wire — seemingly a pig pen — I ...tered the pen and picked up my ball which was marked with green letters. I was not enjoying the game ...t all — in fact was hating it — because of my poor playing and the feeling of helplessness to avert defeat. One of Sperry's drives was an amazing slice which described nearly the course of a boomerang, struck a tree, and bounded forward across the road, almost in ...s original direction. Except for this remarkable slice, and the picking of my ball out of the pig pen, the events of this dream were poorly remembered.

During the summer of 1939 a Smithsonian Insect Biologist recorded 256 dreams on 100 consecutive nights. Because he described his dreams in legible detail and because he illustrated so many of them we have drawn heavily in his journal to establish the distinctive nature of dreaming and to illustrate dream phenomena which we have now studied sistematically. Because he loved trains, we call him the Engine Man.

...railroad station near edge of hole. This station partakes of ...certain characteristics of the stations at Elmira & Solon, but tracks were more as in Cedar Rapids. James & I are standing on platform when we notice a mallet type locomotive (lone) approaching from the right (east), evidently coming through yards to hook on to a train. The engine is too far off to see plainly and is headed toward another set of tracks some distance from us. I say I want to see that engine, & James & I start across tracks to intercept it. I now seem to be hanging on edge of deep hole, & struggling to pull myself up. I am handicapped by numerous "station trucks" which stand close to each other & within 2 or 3 inches of edge. Apparently I succeed in getting up, as I next am hurrying after James who has gone on ahead. I finally catch up, but the engine has already passed from sight. I ask how many drivers the locomotive had and am both surprised & amused to learn that James didn't notice this point — something I would never fail to note.

Our dream lucidity perch is extremely unstable, however, and is connected only by a nerve-like thread to the needle-like flagpole inserted in our cracked carapace. We can't even see, from up there, what is going on inside our bellies, but we may be able to send a message that is sufficiently strong to tip the balance slightly in the direction of pleasure and away from dissolving anxiety. Bosch seems to be saying that we have about as much chance of saving ourselves from slavish instinct as a dreamer has of knowing what is going on and what to do about it. The bizarreness of the image gives us the only clue we have that we are in the grips of the beast that is our cerebral state. The small part of our brain that can awaken - and watch - is our homunculus, even smaller than the owl who sees at night and represents wisdom. But, being on the highest perch of all, he will be the first to fall when the laws of physics (and fate) cause the impossibly ill-balanced fantasy edifice to collapse.

EMOTION: THE INTEGRATIVE FORCE IN DREAMING AND DREAM ART

As incoherent, incongruous, and discontinuous as dream imagery and dream-like imagery in art may be, the fractured parts are held together as much by the unifying power of emotion as by perceptual fusion or artistic synthesis. And the leading dream emotions are fear and anxiety. Most dreams are unpleasant because they are permeated by a sense of foreboding that ranges from the mild disquiet of orientational confusion to the severe panic of dissolution and auto-destruction.

Dreams can also be ecstatic. The question arises why can we only experience positive transports such as joy, elation, and ecstasy rarely, and negative ones such as fear and anxiety so much more commonly? Is this telling us something about how we are constituted? For late medievalists like Bosch, the answer to this question would have to be yes. In the context of traditional Christianity, life was rooted in sin, and damnation had its inevitable consequence. Human beings thus lived in constant fear and dread of their fate. Like the gluttons that rule our stomach or the high-wire acrobat that is our ambition, we will all fall. Fear and anxiety may be said to be the primary emotions that implicitly as well as explicitly bind together the disparate aspects of Bosch's *Tree Man*. What role do they play, we may ask, in the successful binding of the viewer's attention to the drawing?

Anxiety in dreams is often associated with surprise because the bizarreness of successive images continuously seizes our attention. In the Bosch drawing this sequential evocation of anxiety is stimulated by our perception of bizarreness in the work's many details. It is a mild and not unpleasant unease; and it is, as it were, keyed to our amusement at the artist's playful inventiveness. Humor is a similarly common emotional response to our dream reports, even if it is a rare emotion within the dream itself. We are delighted after the fact by the absurd creations of our dreaming brains.

Looking at Bosch's drawing we have the impression that the Tree Man is as amused as he is consternated to be involved in the degrading comedy of existence. Is dream anxiety just a secondary response, as Freud's model of dreaming would have it, or a primary shaper of dream imagery? We have good reason to believe that dream emotions may play at least as important a part in organizing imagery and thought as in constituting reactions to those dream plot elements. In other words, dream anxiety, like dream hallucination, dream delusion, and dream bizarreness are all natural and to a significant extent independent consequences of the biological processes driving the brain-mind in sleep. They are as existential and binding as a man trapped in the form of a tree, or the form of a tree trying to become a man.

DREAM AMNESIA AND THE HYPNOTIC POWER OF DREAM ART

It is safely estimated that at least ninety-five percent and very probably more than ninety-nine percent of our dreams are not recalled at all. Some individuals claim never to have had a single recollection of dreaming in their lives. Does this mean that such individuals - or the better part of most of us - lack imagination? Does it mean that there are dreamless artists? Or that there is dreamless art? Not at all. On the contrary, dreaming is the most extreme and the most instructive of

Man Ray, Dream, 1937, Private Collection.

The drawing is from a notebook that Man Ray kept by his bed, in which on waking he would immediately draw the dreams that he remembered. "In these drawings," he said, "my hands are dreaming."

our auto-creative states. The fact that we don't recall most of our dreams doesn't mean they didn't happen. Laboratory awakening studies validate the assumptions that we dream - vividly - for at least one-and-a-half hours each night, and that less vivid forms of consciousness may occupy another three hours or so.

Science has as much trouble as art in studying or representing something that isn't there. How can dream forgetting be overcome? The enemy, of course, is sleep itself. To remember dreams, we must wake up. And we must wake up quickly and spontaneously, if possible without moving, if we are to capture our fugitive dream visions. It helps to work a bit at dream harvesting. Keeping a journal is a good way to begin. As we ourselves have learned, a bedside notebook, together with a bit of self-hypnosis, can dramatically increase dream recall. The key to success is the suggestion, on going to bed, that one will notice the Bosch-like properties of dream consciousness while the dream is going on; and this recognition will be used to trigger awakening and dream recall. When we take this step, we are not only practicing hypnosis on ourselves - sensitizing our awareness to the bizarre, the hyperassociative, and the visually metaphorical aspects of consciousness - we are also dissociating a small part of our observational minds so that we can get a glimpse of what is going on.

In taking this step, we also become dream artists ourselves. We look over our own shoulders and out from under our complex cerebral machinery. We escape from our jug head single mindedness and take a shy look at our incredible selves. Once we begin to see our dreams we notice that they are as overcharged with imaginative detail as a work by Bosch. We may even find that we cannot possibly record in words all that we see and experience: Words are not the best way to represent sensations, especially the visuo-motor sensa-

tions that typify dreams; and there is simply too much material.

The bizarre complexity of dreams requires more words than ordinary consciousness can muster. A viable alternative is to draw, sketch, or paint our dreams. While living in Paris in the 1930s the American Surrealist artist Man Ray kept a dream journal in the form of pen-and-ink drawings in which he recorded his dream fantasies with an unrestrained hand. Many of these, including the drawing entitled simply *Rêve* (Dream) showing a locomotive in a halo of billowing smoke hurtling to earth above a row of high-rise buildings, were published in 1937 in *Les mains libres*, accompanied by poems of Man Ray's friend Paul Eluard. The book's title - *Free Hands* - was suggested by the artist's statement that "in these drawings my hands are dreaming." He also explained that

I always have by my bed a notebook with pen-and-ink. In the morning when I wake up, if I have dreamed, I sketch my dream immediately.

Clearly Man Ray was not aware of the fact we all dream several times each night of our lives. Had he known this, he would have said not "if I have dreamed," but "if I remembered what I dreamed."

We don't know whether, like Man Ray, the Surrealist author and painter Alberto Savinio kept a dream journal. Be that as it may, Savinio's painting *The Mariner* is a remarkable, evocative image of dream reporting. The mariner is tossed on the waves of sleep, and his dream ship is disoriented as to both time and space. Whether a disembodied, schematically rendered hand is recording his dream or programming it hardly matters. Modern dream science is equally interested in how dreams are formed and how the form of dreams can be recorded and measured. What is most interesting in Savinio's picture is that he has represented automatic writing, the

Pontine Neuronal Firing   (Above) Action potentials from a single pontine giant neuron recorded by microelectrode; (below) pulses (triggered by unit firing) used in computer analysis of unit activity.

method of artistic (or anti-artistic) creation heralded in the early 1920s by André Breton and Philippe Soupoult as being at the very heart of the Surrealist project.

A Modern Dream Artist: The Engine Man

Even for the artistically untalented or untrained, a dream picture is worth at least a thousand dream words. A case in point is the dreamer who was called the Engine Man when his extraordinary dream journal was introduced in *The Dreaming Brain*. To complete the circle from artist to everyman and from everyman to artist, we will here take

another look at his work in the context of dream art and our attempt to access the amusing and informative visual aspect of dreams. Compared to Bosch, the Engine Man's dream drawings are unsophisticated and technically crude; but precisely because they are so unguarded and so obviously honest, these sketches give our more speculative treatment of erudite dream art a very solid base in the dreaming of an ordinary person.

The Engine Man was a well-trained observer of insects. By day he worked as an entomologist at the Smithsonian Institution in Washington, and it was in that city, during the summer of 1939, that he composed the wonderful record of his dreams. He also happened to be inordinately interested in trains, and it was because so many of his dreams reflect this interest that in *The Dreaming Brain* he was called the Engine Man. In one hundred successive nights, working alone at home, he kept a systematic log of his remembered experiences after 256 spontaneous awakenings. As is typical in such cases, his recall quickly increased and during the first two weeks of the experiment his descriptions and drawings became more lengthy and more detailed.

From this exceptional corpus of work we can confirm the presence of all the formal features of dreaming that we have discussed with reference to Bosch's *Tree Man*, except that these are treated more directly, and hence, less metaphorically. For example, while the Engine Man's dream visions were clear and detailed, and so totally convincing that he never doubted that he was awake when he saw them, they were usually not the least bit fantastic and never monstrous. Besides trains, the drawings represented houses, cars, people, furniture, elevators, and - of course - insects. Yet while this subject matter was always commonplace, it was experienced by the dreamer in the same kind of bizarre context fashion that is captured so well in Bosch's drawing.

In the Engine Man's journal, as in laboratory dream reports, the incongruity and discontinuity that is the essence of dream bizarreness was detectable in practically every line of every dream report that was longer than ten lines (or fifty words). This fact establishes beyond a doubt that the awakenings which yielded these reports were of mental experiences associated with the stage of sleep called REM whose features we will describe in chapter 2. And many of the drawings reflected these features too. Thus we see trucks in flower gardens (incongruity) and railroad trestles that stop in mid-air (discontinuity) that are like Bosch's *Tree Man* incongruously floating in a pond.

Complementing these cognitively defective dream features is the imaginative, the inventive, the creative, and the humorous quality which would seem to be the dream's artistic reward for the abandonment of waking-state logic and coherence. And here our Engine Man comes very close to his famous predecessor when this comparison is strictly formal and not a comment on the quality of the drawings. In his Flying Carpet dream, seen on page 76, the Engine Man defies physical law and the image of his dream self hanging on for dear life conveys the same combination of surprise, elation, and fear that the teeter-totter unlikelihood of the jug head construction inspires. Dream life can be dangerous. In his accompanying report, the Engine Man tries to navigate his hover craft to a safe landing and even summons a conspirator with a ladder to help him get off his perilous perch. Dreamers who have played successful memory tricks on themselves and thus regained self-reflective awareness (or lucidity) while doing such death-defying activities as flying may control their fear (after all it is only a dream) and in doing so achieve the insouciance of Bosch's high-wire acrobat.

But the Engine Man's most creative and emotionally significant dream constructions are his *Bicycle Built for Two* (with only one rider), and his *Desk Top Computer* (conceived a quarter century before the personal computer was invented) both seen on page 187. As a comparative zoologist specializing in the classification of insects, our amateur dream artist was faced with the problem of rapid retrieval of the thousands of 5 x 7 notecards which he stored in the six side drawers of his Grand Rapids oak desk. It helped to file them in alphabetical order but he still had to open the drawers and fumble through the cards when he wanted to locate a particular item. At the same time that Alan Turing was developing the principle of the digital computer, the

Engine Man was dreaming up the mechanical information machine seen on page 187. By pushing the appropriate flag on his dream desk, the drawer with the cards describing insects whose species name began with a given letter would spring open.

As a bachelor whose dreams frequently represented his mother, his father, his two sisters, and his nephew - but never a sweetheart - the Bicycle Built for Two dreaming drawing seen on page 187, is a transparent self-portrait of longing, with the lonely entomologist pedaling the front bike seat while the rear one is unoccupied. Whatever the psychodynamics behind the drawing may be, the image is formally bizarre and even exotic. While it is as physically possible as Bosch's *Tree Man*, it is similarly improbable. Imagine the top heaviness caused by the catenary connector of the two dream bicycles. And what would keep the second bike on course? Why wouldn't the whole thing collapse, like the pitcher-ladder on the Tree Man's head?

The suspension of disbelief that we are all prone to in dreams is as clear in the Engine Man's dream drawings as it is the images of Hieronymus Bosch that beguile us with their hypnotic power. What are the intrinsic brain mechanisms which make this pleasant takeover of our minds possible? In the next chapter we shall turn our attention to the neurobiology of REM sleep for possible answers.

Pontine Reticular Formation Giant Cell (Nissl Stain).

The cell body of one of the brain stem neurones shown to be active in REM sleep can be seen in this artistic portrait made by a scientist. Because the aniline dye stains nuclear material intensely, this neurone looks for all the world like an eye but, although it is large compared to other neurones, this cell is actually microscopic in size (50-75 nm in diameter). Scientific research has revealed that neurones like this one may participate in generating eye movements and coordinating them with changes in head, neck, and trunk positions. They may also mediate the startle reflex and the PGO waves of REM sleep. As such, they are among many neuronal architects of mental experiences like dreaming.

Everyman as Artist

The Auto-Creative Mind in Dreaming Sleep

> *The characteristics of sleep, favorable to dreams, are, first, and most important, the predominance in the cerebral machinery of automatic over volitional control.*
>
> Wilhelm Wundt, *Grundlagen der Physiologischen Psychologie (1874)*

While we are awake, our brains and minds are harnessed to pedestrian but essential tasks. Efficient and effective information processing in the service of these tasks is guaranteed by several well-coordinated brain processes that modern sleep research has begun to identify and measure.

They are:

- Activation;
- Input-Output gating;
- Chemical Modulation.

Activation (A) refers to the level of processing capacity of the brain; input-output gating (I) refers to the source of the information processed; modulation (M) refers to the fate of the processed information that depends upon brain chemistry. A three dimensional state space shows how these processes interact to generate the sleep-wake cycle.

To help the reader understand the processes of activation and neuromodulation and how they are relevant to image generation in dreaming and in art, it will be useful to look at paintings that seem to us to illustrate directly what we take these terms to mean. We will return to the process of input-output gating later in this chapter.

The Birth of the World by the Spanish Surrealist Juan Miró illustrates activation by focusing on the elemental compositional level of image formation.

I and the Village by the Russian Cubist-inspired Marc Chagall illustrates neuromodulation in its reorganization of the rules of spatio-temporal order in helter-skelter, imaginative juxtaposition of scenes from the artist's childhood.

Like the hypothetical puddle in which life began when lightning struck it, Miró's *The Birth of the World* is an inchoate world of free-floating energy with the capacity of creating its own order. This innate energy is the essence of activation. It is inherent in every cell in the body and its regulation is the specialized responsibility of the brain. It is easy

Juan Miró, *The Birth of the World*, 1925, The Museum of Modern Art, New York.

The painting shows an inchoate world of free-floating energy with the capacity of creating its own order of new and unpredictable configurations. This artistic process can be linked to the process of neuronal activation in the dreaming brain.

to understand how this daily pulse of brain activation keeps the body in harmony with the ebb and flow of energy from the sun. But pulses of brain activation also punctuate sleep, causing the mind to recombine is own primordial elements into new and unpredictable configurations. Some scientists think that this kind of brain activation helps to keep us in harmony with ourselves - with our biological, psychological, and social histories and destinies.

One model that helps us understand the brain process called modulation is the audio tape recorder. Another is the fairy tale painting *I and the Village* by Marc Chagall. In fact, we need only think of fairy tales themselves to get the point. In fairy tales the usual modes of time, place, and even person are changed so that impossible, or at least highly improbably things can and do happen. The fantastic and magical mode replaces the reality mode in order that basic characteristics of human behavior, human emotion, and human destinies can be made. The work of Chagall illustrates this mode shift with particular clarity.

In *I and the Village* background and foreground distinctions are lost exactly as they are in the mind of the dreamer as a result of the mechanism of demodulation in REM sleep dreaming. Chagall's internal spatio-temporal memory landscape evokes a sense of functional unity between the village's human, plant, and animal worlds. The human nose and the muzzle of a beast approach each other in the center of the composition. Below, a sprig is offered in a matrimonial gesture, and elsewhere the theme of husbandry is developed: a cow is milked (inside its own head), and above to the left a man with a scythe and a woman are working in a field. The symmetrical inversion of the couple in the field, and the jumps in scale from the human and animal profiles to the miniature figures within and between them makes the same sort of aesthetic and emotional sense as the displace-ments and incongruities in dreams. The net effect is to draw us into a world whose incongruities and discontinuities are, as in dreams, highly involving and powerfully moving. This is the dream mode which in sleep is caused by the chemical modulation of the brain.

The processes of activation and neuromodulation by which the brain-mind becomes auto-creative in sleep are universal, powerfully preemptive, and specifiable at the deep biological level of (neurones) brain cells and chemical molecules (neurotransmitters) that neurones use to signal to one another. It is important to point out that these phenomena have been identified most clearly in the study of sleep in cats, not humans. But cats like most other mammals, share our pattern of sleep, in which waking first gives way to sleep unconsciousness, and then changes again to guarantee intense, vivid, and bizarre dreaming.

These deep and precious animal-based findings were made after the severe limits of the techniques used in studying neurobiology of human sleep were recognized in the early 1960s. They have recently been complemented by the development of new neuroimaging techniques, which allow scientists better to define the activation process by revealing regional differences. Brain activation and deactivation, which was first thought to be global on the basis of EEG studies in humans, and was later revealed to be regionally differentiated in animals, has now been shown to be regionally differentiated in humans as well.

Recent neuro-imaging research has demonstrated that the dreaming brain shows more activation of brain areas concerned with emotion and with complex visual image generation, and less activation of brain areas concerned with memory, self-reflective awareness, and directed thought. The implications of these findings for dream theory are self-evident. We will try to extend them to a new theory of the making and experiencing of art.

As we have said in chapter 1, we do not

Marc Chagall, I and the Village, 1911, The Museum of Modern Art, New York.

Chagall has obliterated distinctions of foreground and background, scale, location, and direction (the cow being milked inside its own head at the upper left, the symmetrical inversion of the couple at the upper right), as they are in dreams, due to the modulations in the brain during sleep.

imply either that art is created in the dream state, or that art is necessarily dream-like. What we do mean is that the human brain-mind is intrinsically auto-creative and that the processes by which dreaming is guaranteed are germane to our general understanding of art and to dream art in particular. While these processes are clearly recognizable in sleep, they are also operative to greater or lesser extent and are more or less easily accessed the waking state.

The Discovery of REM Sleep Dreaming

The fact that brain activation is a critical determinant of the level of conscious experience was scientifically broached by the studies of Giuseppe Moruzzi and Horace Magoun in the late 1940s. Using the electroencephalograph (or EEG) as an index, it was possible to show that the activation asociated with waking could be experimentally induced by electrically stimulating the relatively primitive brainstem, a deep structure connecting the spinal cord to the upper brain seats of emotion and cognition. These upper brain regions include the limbic lobes (the seat of emotion) and cerebral cortex (the center of perception and cognition) that we assume are necessary to the making and enjoyment of art. For either to occur a switch in our brainstems must be turned on. So far, so good, but only indirectly relevant to a theory of dreaming.

Directly relevant to dreaming was the 1953 discovery by Eugene Aserinsky and Nathaniel Kleitman that the same EEG signs of global brain activation that were associated with waking could also be observed to occur, spontaneously, at intervals of 90-100 minutes in sleep. Associated with this objective evidence of brain activation in sleep was eye movement. Under still closed lids, the eyes darted back and forth, up and down, and even

around in circles. The unmistakable and paradoxical import was that a part of the brain was waking up but the rest of it, as well as the body, was not.

The scientists then did an obvious thing. When they saw the EEG evidence of brain activation and the rapid eye movements they woke their subjects up. And when they did they elicited descriptions of images and plots with all of the formal properties of dreaming which we have described in chapter 1 and illustrated in the *Tree Man* by Hieronymus Bosch and the dream drawings of Man Ray and the Engine Man. Because the eye movements were abrupt and fast, and because they continued for periods of five to fifty minutes in duration, Aserinsky and his colleagues called this phase of sleep REM (for rapid eye movement) and advanced the radical theory that it constituted the physiological basis of human dreaming.

How could the paradoxical co-existence of brain activation and sleep be understood? When that switch in our brainstem is thrown on, why don't we just wake up? There are three answers to this question:

(1) External sensations are actively locked out and internally generated motor commands are locked in.

(2) The chemical constitution of the brain is altered by the selective inactivation of brainstem neurones that give the waking brain its powers of attention, logic, and memory. This is what we mean by neuromodulation. The neuromodulatory systems which are inactivated in REM sleep are those which secrete norepinephrine and serotonin. These neurones are called aminergic because norepinephrine and serotonin are biogenic amines.

(3) Certain parts of the brain are then hyperactivated. These include the emotion centers in the limbic lobe and areas of cerebral cortex involved in the integration of emotion with perception. Other parts are contrastingly deactivated, most interestingly the frontal

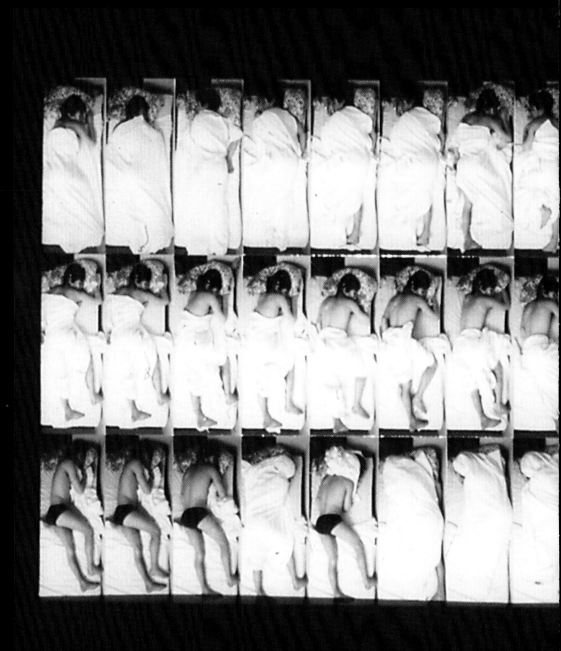

Peter Sleeps in the Lab.

Despite the availability of time-lapse photographic techniques of Edward Muybridge and Jules-Etienne Marey, who worked in Freud's time at the end of the 19th century, it was almost a century before sleep was the subject of photographic study by the late Theodore Spagna. Spagna's work spanned a wide variety of human and animal subjects sleep in natural, captive, and laboratory settings and revealed a clear pattern of posture shifts which were the behavioral read outs of the internal and automatic changes in brain state that underlie the NREM-REM cycle. As indicated by the frequent posture shifts, Peter did not sleep well in the three hours shown here.

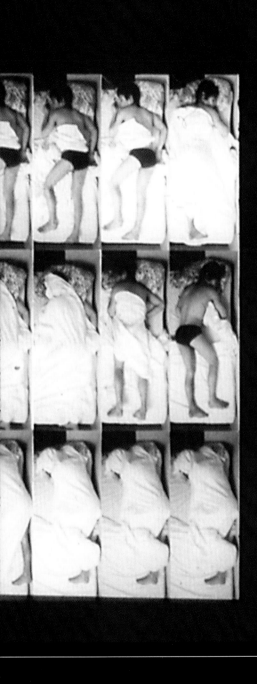

cortex zones known to be essential to memory, critical judgment, and directed thought. This is what we mean by regional activation and deactivation. Together with this general activation is an increase, to waking levels, of the neuromodulators, acetylcholine and dopamine.

We know now that in order to have waking consciousness with its capacity to collect, evaluate, and act on external data we must activate the brain including the frontal cortex, open the gates of sensation and motion, and perfuse the activated brain with specific chemical molecules.

If we want to go to sleep - even while reading a book or listening to a lecture we don't quite understand - we need to deactivate the brain, including the frontal cortex. We need to begin closing the gates of sensation and motion. And we need to subtract from the unconscious brain the modulators of attention and memory. In this way we can exclude, ignore, and forget the outside world.

In order now to move our minds to the extraordinary capacity to generate internal perceptions (hallucinations) of convincing reality (delusions), and equip these dream forms with peculiar contextual qualities (bizarreness) and strong emotion (especially anxiety), but not remember them (amnesia), we must activate the parts of the brain that perceive complex images and link them to emotion, and turn off the parts that enable us to evaluate, act upon, and recall these exotic scenarios. This is the neurobiological definition of the brain state that is the ideal substrate of dreaming.

ENTER THE NEURONES!
OUR MICROSCOPIC SELVES

Like all other parts of the body, the brain is comprised of cells. But the nerve cells, or neurones, that make up our brains are unique-

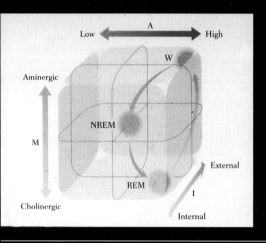
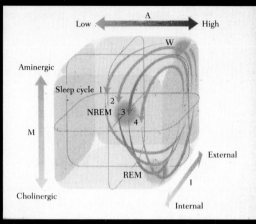

AIM Model of Conscious State Control.

A three dimensional model plots the value of A (for activation) against the

values of I (for input source) and of M (for modulation) to give a point in the resulting 3-dimension state space. In time (the 4th dimension),

the AIM points move from the waking domain (high A, low I, high M) through the NREM sleep domain to the REM sleep domain (high A, high I, low M)

following an elliptical trajectory that repeats itself four times a night.

ly specialized for the acquisition, transfer, and storage of information. These important processes are achieved by way of structural refinements:

(1) Acquisition of information depends upon the dynamic response of the membrane that surrounds each cell and is modified so that it can faithfully convert external information like light and color in the retina of the eye into its own codes.

(2) The transfer of the transduced information depends upon each neurone's capacity to encode the external data into a sequence of discrete electrical signals, called action potentials, which from that moment on, constitute the language of the brain. Light energy never gets beyond the retina, and sound energy never gets beyond the ear drum.

(3) The storage of this neuronally encoded language is still something of a mystery, but it clearly involves the brain's ability to modify its internal chemical structure in such a way as to keep a record of its experience which can then affect its future responsiveness.

THE ART OF BRAIN SCIENCE

Before going further with the scientific exposition of our story, we would like to emphasize some aesthetic aspects of neurobiology. The aesthetic response of neurobiologists to the structure and function of the brain is a component of their fascination and motivation in studying the physiology of the brain. One hears the word "beautiful" used by those who explore its exquisite structure (the neuroanatomists), its electrical signals (the neurophysiologists), its response to drugs (the neuropharmacologists), and its organized activity that results in behavior (the neuroethologists) and in awareness (the neuropsychologists). Most modern neuroscientists use more than one of these approaches, and they see beauty at each level of analysis.

The brain is a natural work of art of such astonishing beauty that it is inconceivable that its capacities do not include the aesthetic response that we have to it, and the ability to create beautiful renderings of its own expe-

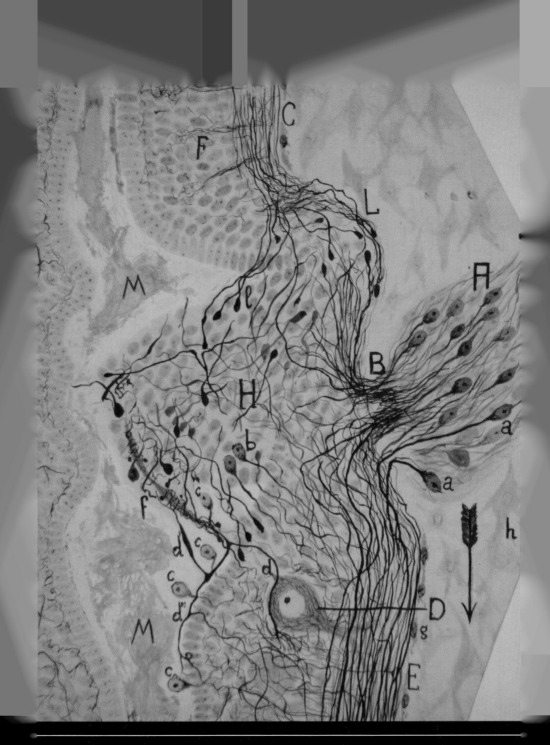

on y Cajal- *Spinal Cord*
neration.

Spanish
obiologist, Santiago
on y Cajal, won the
el Prize for discovering
each brain cell (or
one) was a discrete

unit. His microscopic
studies were illustrated by
drawings (instead of
photographs) because he
believed that the more
active form of recording of
brain structures would lead
to a greater intuitive
understanding of brain

function. He (and his
students) used India ink
pens and camel hair
brushes to represent
nervous processes (black)
and cell contents (half-
tone gray). In this
painting, he is showing the
regrowth of cells after the

experimental disruption
connections. The Caja
arrow indicating the he
end of the animal is a
hallmark of work done
his institute in Madrid.

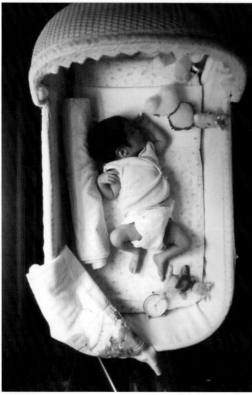

Sleeping Eros, Roman copy of Greek original, 3rd century BC, Galleria degli Uffizi, Florence.

During the Hellenistic period the god of love Eros, often represented as a winged, sleeping Cupid, was also the bearer of dreams. In his right hand he is holding two capsules of poppy seeds, the opium from which was used for making sleeping potions and inducing dreams.

Baby Sleep - Theodore Spagna.

The ability to recognize the NREM and REM phases in the posture shifts of sleep begins in the REM-rich period of postnatal development. Human babies sleep twice as long as adults (16 vs. 8 hrs) and twice as much of their sleep time is devoted to REM (45% to 20%). That means that after birth, when the brain is developing rapidly, the infant spends as much time in REM (8 hrs) as it does awake! An inescapable hypothesis is that REM sleep serves brain development.

rience in the form of dreams and works of art. The exploration of these renderings, which depend upon the brain's capacity to dream, is the focus of this book. Our objective is to describe from the bottom up the processes by which such tiny structures as neurones are agents of such elaborate creations as dreams, works of art, and images of angels. Facing this daunting task, it is easy to understand why so many of our predecessors assigned dream instigation to the winged messengers of the Gods.

Neuronal Interaction and Emergent Properties

Neurones may be tiny, but they are numerous. There are 100 billion of them, by the current estimate. This means that there are more discrete elements in each of our brains than there are humans on earth. But the collectivity of neurones is much more favorably organized than global society because all neurones speak the same basic electrochemical language: they are intensely interconnected, and they are governed by an enlightened central hierarchy. The fact that each neurone can talk fast (up to 60 messages per second) and to so many of its neighbors (up to 10,000) at a time sounds like a formula for chaos, and it is. But in the case of the brain, chaos is essential for two of our most highly valued attributes, self-organization and creativity.

In order to understand how the brain works, we first need to grasp some simple organizational principles that will get us from single cells and molecules to harmoniously regulated states like waking, sleep, and dreaming. Later on we will turn the system loose and see what it can produce in the way of fantastic landscapes and dream divinations.

The path that each human brain takes in forming itself is a good way to start. Each neurone comes into the world equipped with its own complete genomic game plan. The trick is to select the play, and to teach each player his moves. As far as we know, there is no coach, no master architect, and no supervisory agenda. In brief, there are no angels in the head. Rather than being instructed by angels, the neurones that support consciousness invent angels to explain their own existence.

Genetic information, however vast - and rich beyond imagining - cannot possibly account for much more than a crude layout of each neurone's position in the brain, its signaling capability, its receptivity, and its chemical identity. The primordial system that is the human embryo-fetus evinces surprisingly early (within fifteen to twenty weeks) both irritability (responsiveness to stimuli) and spontaneous activity (unstimulated movement). Moreover, these properties are organized and appear with such rhythmic regularity that we can confidently call them behaviors.

By twenty-seven weeks, fetal behavior is dominated by a recurrent organizational state that has been tentatively identified as the primordium of REM sleep. That doesn't mean that the fetus is dreaming, but it does mean that the neurobiology of REM emerges very early in human development, and this implies that it plays an active, autocreative role in our early brain development.

We still know very little of the detailed mechanics of REM processes. But we do know that they bring us into the world with an ongoing capacity to enter a self-determined, self-organizing state called REM sleep which stays with us throughout our lives, playing a decreasingly prominent role in our continuing physical and mental development. In the first year of life we spend eight hours a day in REM, a figure that will drop four-fold by the time we are mature enough to go to college and thereafter decline slowly in parallel with the brain's lifelong degenerative course. There are several important morals to this story. One is that the brain cre-

Willem de Kooning, Untitled XIII, 1985, The Cleveland Museum of Art, Leonard Hanna, Jr. Fund.

After contracting Alzheimer's disease in the 1980s, bereft of memory and guided, as in dreaming, by motoric automatisms, de Kooning was still capable, in contrast to his strident, turbulent, multi-layered paintings prior to the onset of Alzheimer's, of producing clear, balanced, untroubled decorative compositions.

ates itself - beautifully, as we have emphasized - and continues to recreate itself as long as we live. To the extent that we can nourish, support, and profit from these innate processes we can be said to be present at the creation. One of the functions that this auto-creative process ensures is creativity itself. In our dreams and in our art we celebrate these biological mechanisms while we wait for brain science to tell us more about how they work.

Brain Death and Dream Art

Even after parts of the brain that we could intuitively suppose to be essential to artistic creation are dead, the brain remains auto-creative and even artistically competent, as the curious case of Willem de Kooning clearly demonstrates. In the course of the 1980s, after Alzheimer's disease had begun to deprive him of the capacity for oriented, self-reflective, and directed waking consciousness, the artist was capable of producing colorful abstract paintings. Bereft of memory (as in a dream) and guided by spontaneous, highly developed instinctive motoric automatisms (as in dreaming), the decorticated artist created clear, untroubled, balanced compositions.

The point we wish to make is that de Kooning did not need his frontal lobes for anything more than learning how to paint and choosing what to paint. Once he knew how to paint that skill was relegated to his subcortical brain where automatic motor activity and visual imagery are integrated with emotion as they are in dreams. Commenting on de Kooning's works of the 1980s, Oliver Sachs has reported that the preservation of aesthetic and artistic feeling is a fundamental trait even of advanced stages of Alzheimer's, to the extent that persons who have become incapable of verbal expression have done remarkable paintings.

We don't wish to imply that the play of the cortically based intellect doesn't contribute to the making of art. What the case of de Kooning shows is that the parts of the brain that are engaged in REM sleep dreaming can still serve the artist after the parts that are disengaged are gone. From this it would follow that the subcortical dreaming brain is also crucial to the success of elaborate, iconographically complex works such as the *Tree Man* by Hieronymus Bosch.

The Dreaming Brain and the Creative Process in Art

Since sleep science had shown that brain activation could occur in both waking and in REM sleep, and that brain activation could be experimentally triggered by electrical stimulation of the brainstem, it was natural to wonder if REM sleep brain activation also emanated from the brainstem. The experiments of Michel Jouvet in Lyon indicated that it did, and that the brain activation of sleep depended upon roughly the same areas of the so-called reticular formation that were important for waking. Jouvet's seminal work added two other processes to brain activation: input-output gating and chemical neuromodulation. Because they too were also brainstem functions, it was possible to begin framing a brain-based dream theory in terms of brainstem physiology, and to construct a neurobiological model of the dreaming brain.

The general idea was that dreaming would be favored if the brain were internally activated (if its constituent neurones were made to fire more vigorously) but remained off-line (if its activated neurones could generate their own information but not receive information from or transmit information to the outside world), and if its neurones were chemically altered (if they were made to process internally generated information in a unique way). This is the outline structure of the AIM model and the activation-synthesis hypothesis that we will describe in detail further on in this chapter, and use as a guiding hypothesis of our discussion of dream art in the balance of the book. Before doing so, however, we need to give an account of some of the specialized neuronal systems that organize our brains in such a way as to make dreaming and auto-creativity possible.

CHEMICAL NEUROMODULATION

In the early 1960s three important scientific advances coalesced to advance our understanding of ourselves. The first was Jouvet's discovery that the triggering mechanism for REM sleep was in the pontine brainstem. That meant that there had to be a neuronal switch that turned on and off during sleep to produce the reliable periodic alternation of REM and NREM (non-REM) epochs. But how was the neuronal switch constructed? How did it turn on and off? What was its wiring diagram? The answers to these questions led to two other discoveries.

Using anatomical methods that could determine the chemical flavor of neurones by causing them to fluoresce when dye-stained, the swedish scientists Kjell Fuxe and Anica Dahlstrom discovered that most of the brain's internal chemical control systems were also located in the brainstem. Of course, every neurone uses chemicals to communicate with its colleagues, but brainstem neurones were unique in several ways, the most important of which is that the kind of chemical they use doesn't represent specific information about the outside world or dictate a motor response. Instead, their chemicals, specifically norepinephrine, serotonin, acetylcholine, and dopamine tell the cells what to do with such signals, including whether or not to remember them.

Because of this capacity to alter the mode of brain information processing, these brainstem neurones were called modulatory,

and their chemically modulated function was called neuromodulation. Hence, the term chemical neuromodulation. The easiest way to comprehend this function is by way of an analogy between the mode of neuromodulation and the mode control switch on an electronic device which can either record or play back, but not do both at once. The brain can do either, or both, or neither, depending on the level and quality of neuromodulation. Whether or not (and how much or how little) these chemical neuromodulatory cells are active makes a huge difference to brain function. Michel Jouvet immediately seized upon this discovery and began to try to figure out how the neuromodulatory cells influence waking, sleeping, and dreaming by administering drugs that were exactly like those that are used so widely in psychiatry today to raise or lower the levels of brain activation and deactivation. The effects were dramatic, but difficult to interpret.

MAKING CONTACT WITH THE NEURONES

In order to clarify the situation, it was important to be able to record directly from the neuromodulatory neurones. But how could this be done? Although they sent their chemical modulators to all parts of the brain, the cell bodies lay deep in the brainstem far from the surface of the brain. Furthermore, they were very small and very few in number compared to their neuronal neighbors that were engaged in the more traditional business of activating the brain and of input-output signal processing.

This problem was solved by the ingenuity of two neurobiologists, David Hubel and Edward Evarts. Because they both wanted to unlock the mystery of sleep by recording from individual nerve cells, they developed a move-

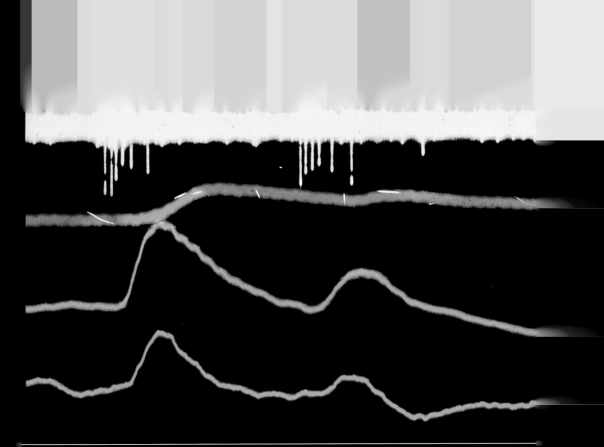

PGO Cells.

As we lie asleep in our beds and our eyes move to the right or left, our brains process movement associated signals. This is dramatically true of the thalamic relay nucleus called the lateral geniculate body) and the posterolateral cortex where visual perception is thought to occur. This cat peribrachial cell fires a burst (upper trace) prior to both larger (same side) and smaller (opposite side) waves in the visual thalamus (lower traces). The bursts of firing of this single peribrachial neuron (green trace) can be seen to precede each eye movement (blue trace) and the PGO waves in the geniculate bodies (orange trace). Note also that the size of the PGO wave in the two geniculates differs: the geniculate wave on the same side of the brain as the peribrachial burst cell and the side to which the eyes are moving is always larger than the geniculate wave on the opposite side It seems likely that the internal visualization of dreams depends upon such self stimulation.

able micro-electrode recording system that makes Bosch's tray-pitcher-ladder assembly ine look like a child's toy. The Hubel-Evarts toy went down deep into the brain, but only when instructed to do so by a scientist who was then able to sample the electrical signal properties of individual neurones and record them on tape for later quantitative analysis. Because the brain itself is insensitive, it was possible to introduce these probes into its depth during natural states of waking and sleep.

At first, this system was used to assess the levels of activation and inactivation of neu ronal populations engaged in vision and movement; later it was applied to those brain cells that were engaged in associative integra tion. To everyone's great surprise, it was soon clear that although the net level of activation of all of these systems declined by twenty to fifty percent when animals went to sleep, they did not stop functioning altogether. Further more, almost all of them resumed their wak ing levels when the animals entered REM even though the animals did not wake up Looking at the activity of the neurones alone you would not be able easily to distinguish between waking and dreaming. So either there is something else going on - like an angel saying, "You aren't awake, this is just a dream," or the neuronal activation patterns of waking and sleep are altered in some other physical way. You can guess by now that this way turns out to be chemical neuromodulation.

THE BIRTH OF NEURONAL DREAM THEORY

But there was another problem that the neurones had to solve: How to create internal perceptions of convincing reality and how to block real motor responses to them. Without these two mechanisms we would not be able to dream. Instead of dreaming, we would wake up. The moveable micro-electrode technique, together with a few other neurobiological tricks, soon enabled sleep scientists to show that the motor blockade was achieved by actively inhibiting motor command neurones in the spinal cord with chemical signals from the brainstem. This left the motor systems of the upper brain free to indulge in whatever make-believe movement they chose. Their commands would simply be ignored because the dreamer was paralyzed.

Dream vision is more complicated and more surprising. What seems to happen is that neurones in the upper brain that generate complex imagery in waking are not only turned on in REM but are also driven by internal stimuli arising in or near the eye movement centers of the brain stem. The theory that has been advanced holds that the eye movement command system sends sensory information about its intentions to the vision centers which then generate images in response to them: "I move my eyes, therefore I see."

Recent brain imaging studies in humans point to regions of interest for this hypothesis of visual image generation and for the integration of such images with emotion and memory. Because these regions are at a high level of information processing and because they are very near the emotion mediating centers, one implication is that dream vision is not built up from tiny scraps of data, as it is in waking when we decompose details of the visual world and then recombine them in the brain. Perhaps that is why dream imagery is not kaleidoscopic. In its complex intensity it is, rather hyper real and even surreal. Further neurobiological work on this system is likely to help us answer Leonardo da Vinci's famous question: "Why does the eye see a thing more certainly in dreams than the imagination when awake?"

The Italian for "more certain" is più certa, which can also be translated as "more real" or "more vivid." For Leonardo visual perception was the foundation of knowledge. But as the art historian Henri Zerner has pointed out, perception by itself is not the whole of vision. "Vision" also includes the power of the imagination to give visual form to the fantasies and conceptions of the mind. It was through the visualizing power of the mind that Leonardo wanted to give the representation of the world, whether real or not, the vividness of dreams.

Some experimental evidence already suggests that one cause for the hyperclarity of dreams may be that the internal image generator is not only more active than in waking, but that it is even more active than the external image generator in the waking state. We have two good reasons to believe that the external image generation system has precedence and priority over internal image generation in normal waking. One is that we see the world remarkably well when we are awake, and the second is that we do not normally hallucinate in that state. In fact, while we can easily summon visual images without closing our eyes while awake, these are but pale copies of our truly hallucinatory dream images. In order to enhance such internal visionary experiences, be they meditative, hypnotic, or oneiric, it is crucial to decrease attention to external perception and, inversely, to focus on internal perception. The brain does this for us by input-output gating, a mechanism that is most powerfully and clearly in operation in REM sleep dreaming. ·

THE DREAM ANGEL AND NEURONAL CONSTRAINTS ON DREAM ARTISTS

We owe many of our insights in regard to internal stimulus generation to Michel Jouvet, who made still another capital discovery in his early animal studies. Using only the relatively insensitive method of electroencephalography, Jouvet found that by placing electrodes deep in the signal centers of the brain (rather than on the scalp or brain surface) he could detect internally generated signals, which he called PGO waves because they had their origin in the pons (P) and then radiated to the geniculate body of the thalamus (G) and finally to the occipital cortex (O). We now know the chemical mechanisms of this system, but before detailing them, some general points need to be emphasized.

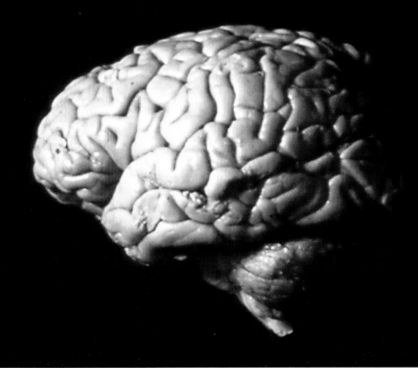

Brain form Dreamstage.

Outside the chamber in which the Dreamstage sleeper lay, we placed a human brain so that visitors would understand that modern sleep science has begun to establish an internal physical basis for sleep and dreaming. The human brain contains 100 billion individual cells (or neurones), each of which communicated with about 10,000 others at message rates of 2-60 per second. A modest estimate of the information processing capacity of the brain is 10^{27} bits per second.

The first is that the PGO waves of REM sleep look like those seen in brains afflicted with epilepsy. As such they clearly constitute strong and pre-emptive internal activation signals. When PGO waves are emitted the brain is co-opted. It is parasitized. It is invaded by alien signals from its own depths. When we dream, we are quite literally seized - like Fyodor Dostoyevsky in the throes of his temporal lobe epilepsy - and thus prompted to elaborate mad, fearsome dream plots, like those that became *Crime and Punishment* and *The Brothers Karamazov*. Furthermore, while the PGO waves can be elicited in waking by strong, novel stimuli, they are quickly suppressed when the stimuli are repeated. These two points can be combined in the concept that PGO waves reflect activity of a system that is strongly inhibited in waking, but much more indiscriminately activated in REM sleep. No wonder we run amok in our dreams.

If we wanted to turn this PGO system on in visitors to an art gallery or a theater the best way to do so would be to create an inter-

John Anster Fitzgerald, The Artist's Dream, 1857, Private Collection, United Kingdom.

The dreaming artist is assailed by drug-induced hallucinations of bizarre elves and goblins that resemble the metamorphic monsters of Marcantonio's Dream of Raphael (see page 92). The artist in the painting is the Victorian fairy painter Fitzgerald himself, and the beautiful fairy who is the model for the picture on which he is working in his dream is the heroine of the romantic ballet Sylphide.

nally incoherent but emotionally potent image (or a sequence of images) that would activate the neurones by eliciting surprise and anxiety; this would force an active effort to orient and comprehend, an effort that would be further confounded by either a wealth of bizarre detail in the image, a wildly incoherent juxtaposition of banal images, or an incoherent, discontinuous sequence of such images. We will try to show that this is exactly what dream art actually does. We will also suggest that even art that has nothing explicitly to do with dreams may trigger startle responses.

But how, we may now ask, is the brain transformed from its daytime photojournalist mode to its nighttime dramaturgic role? The still very incomplete but exciting answer is that the brain changes its mind by changing its chemistry. We have already noted that the photojournalistic functions of waking, like the capacity to observe, describe, depict, and analyze events even as they are performed depends upon activation of the brain, upon opening its sensory and motor gates, and - most critically - upon supplying it with the appropriate chemical modulators so that the storyline is kept linear and logical.

When the two aminergic modulators, norepinephrine and serotonin, become less and less available - owing to active inhibition of the brainstem neurones that manufacture and deliver them to other neurones - we can no longer perform our observational, reportorial, and behavioral roles. As we fall asleep and the activation level declines, the sensory and motor gates close in unison with the progressive cessation of signaling by two groups of cells: the locus coeruleus (which makes norepinephrine) and the raphé nuclei (which make serotonin).

These two cell groups are admirably well suited to do their job of creating the ideal chemical conditions for waking. In addition to their strategic location in the transition between the upper brain (where consciousness resides) and the spinal cord (which reports in and reads out its messages), these tiny little cells are chock full of wake-up chemicals. And they can be counted on to supply them at a consistent level because they share the property of automatic spontaneous discharge with the pacemaker cells of the heart. Instead of firing only when told to do so (like the information processing cells that they modulate) they fire unless they are told not to do so. They have a mind of their own, as it were, and thanks to them, so do we. Because it may be hard to see how such automaticity results in mental freedom, we will return to this point in our later discussions of creativity.

For the present, our main point is that for the powers of awareness (including self-awareness), criticism (including self-criticism), and analysis (including self-analysis), we must be grateful to a surprisingly limited number of small neurones in our brainstems. These are the patrons, the benefactors - the angels if you will - of waking cognition. They are the patrons of the arts in the sense that to make works of art and to evaluate the aesthetic merit of artwork depends upon these heart-like brain cells doing their slavish job.

THE NEURONAL CLOCKS THAT TIME OUR BRAINS

The reason that most people stop working at night is that the brain works differently at night from its mode of operation during the day. The tendency to wake by day and sleep by night is caused by a clock in a part of the brain called the hypothalamus which is a pacemaker in a very different sense. The beat (or rhythm) of this neuronal clock is about 24 hours, a time interval which is genetically encoded within the DNA of the

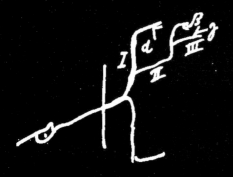

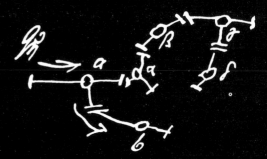

Freud's Neurone Drawings.

To illustrate his Project for a Scientific Psychology, Freud made sketches of neurones as he understood them.

Individual cells complete with dendrites and axons, look remarkably like modern Golgi preparations but his circuitry is fancifully designed to illustrate his

"side path" concept of the unconscious. According to Freud, the nervous impulses that were unacceptable to consciousness were diverted into side paths

from which they caused both neurosis and dreams. Freud's antiquated ideas of the nervous system thus adversely affected his dream theory.

---

hypothalamic neurones. The exact daily onset time of their activation is set by light, as is waking; and when they are active, so are the chemical neuromodulatory pacemaker cells of the brainstem.

At nocturnal sleep onset, after the waking functions of the brain have shut down and the brain's portals have been closed, the neuromodulatory cells continue to fire and to time an unimaginably beautiful and dramatic set of changes. It turns out that the hypothalamic 24 hour pacemaker interacts with the brainstem neuromodulatory neurones. After sleep onset, the brainstem system is subjected to progressively increasing inhibition which after a delay of 30 minutes in cats and 90 minutes in humans, completely shuts down the aminergic wake state modulators. At the

same time, the acetylcholine containing neurones turn back on, perhaps due to loss of inhibitory restraint from the aminergic neurones.

Because of its strong and direct correlation with REM, acetylcholine is as close as we can now come to naming the brain's dream angel or at least its annunciatory voice. Dopamine, which is secreted at equally high levels in all brain states, may help too. The function of acetylcholine in the brain includes direct responsibility for generalized activation; and this helps us explain the brain activation of REM which sets the stage for dreaming. Acetylcholine also appears to be intimately involved with the most specific of all REM signs, the PGO waves, which activate specific systems of the emotive visual image and associative generators in a pseudo-sensory fashion. In fact, the uninhibited and unbalanced activation of the acetylcholine (cholinergic) system signals contributes to the mental functions which are enhanced in dreaming. These are the hallucinatory visual and motor perceptions, the emotions of anxiety, elation, and anger, and the hyperassociative combination of such elements into a fantastic scenario.

The waking state functions that become deficient in dreaming, such as the failure of self-reflective awareness, the delusional acceptance of improbable and impossible events, the loss of constancy of time, place, and person, and - most critically - of the directive power of thought, may be due to the loss of norepinephrine and/or serotonin.

Reciprocal Interaction and Dreaming

The question now is whether acetylcholine enhancement and norepinephrine/serotonin deficiency have something to do with each other. Are they somehow reciprocal? And are the mental functions that are altered correspondingly reciprocal? The answer to all three of these questions is yes. When the subtraction from the waking brain of its critical controlling chemicals, norepinephrine and serotonin, was recognized in the mid-1970s, neurophysiologists assumed that its inhibition would very probably provoke the dynamic release of another neuromodulatory system. The cholinergic system was for many reasons a likely candidate. Now that candidacy is secure thanks to a widely replicated set of experiments which has allowed scientists to bring REM sleep under chemical control.

The experiments that demonstrated the capacity of drugs which initiate or empower natural acetylcholine to trigger REM sleep immediately from waking and to produce enhancement of REM and/or PGO waves for days or even weeks are still being pursued. They are important not only to the chemistry of dreaming but are also part of an effort to understand how REM can promote such diverse functions as body temperature and dietary caloric control, consolidation of memory, and regulation of mood. For a detailed exposition of these experiments the reader is referred to Allan Hobson's books, *Dreaming as Delirium* (1999), *The Dream Drug Store* (2001), and *Out of Its Mind: Psychiatry in Crisis* (2001). All of the experiments were inspired by the reciprocal interaction model of REM sleep control proposed by Allan Hobson and Robert McCarley in 1975. Since the model is also the foundation of the dream theory called activation-synthesis, we summarize it here.

Critical cognitive functions of the waking state require that the cortex, the thalamus, and the limbic systems of the upper brain be continuously modulated by norepinephrine and serotonin. Arousal, attention, critical analysis, and directed thought all depend on the continuous availability of these modulatory chemicals to upper brain circuits, especially those of the frontal lobes. Because the brainstem neurones which supply these chemicals are pacemaker cells, their firing is regular and reliable unless they are inhibited, as they are at sleep onset, by sleep initiating neurones in the hypothalamus. When they are active, the acetylcholine system functions collaboratively with them but is restrained by inhibition of its own neuronal sources, especially serotonin.

As the inhibition of the acetylcholine systems by serotonin and norepinephrine declines during NREM sleep, the cholinergic neurones become increasingly excitable. As they increase their discharge rate, these neurones gradually activate the upper brain and then stimulate it via the PGO system associated with the REMs.

Other brainstem neurones actively inhibit

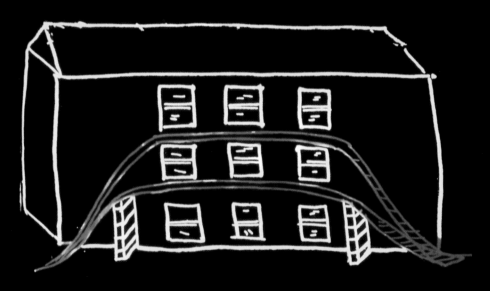

Truck and Custom House Drawings from the Engine Man's Dream Journal.

Dream bizarreness is depicted in these drawings from the Engine Man's Dream Journal. The truck in a garden and the customs house with ramps on the outside are both classic exemples of dream plot incongruity. These amateur artistic efforts convey the same aspects of dream formalism that can be seen in the more sophisticated work of artists like Paul Delvaux (see the railway trestle in the center of Delvaux's *L'Ecole des Savants* on page 14 and the rose in the cityscape of *Pandora's Box* by René Magritte on page 148).

muscle tone (making trunk and limb movement impossible) and actively inhibit sensory messages from the environment (guaranteeing the continuation of sleep in the face of the activation of the brain). The net result is a REM sleep brain (and a dreaming mind) which is turned on but which can process only data arising within its own confines because it is actively kept off-line to external information. The body is actively paralyzed and cannot move even if motor commands are issued. Furthermore and finally, the activated, gate closed brain cannot process its internal data in the usual way because it lacks the chemicals necessary to create the orderly, linear, associative processing necessary for attention, orientation, directed thought, and critical judgment.

ACTIVATION SYNTHESIS AND PSYCHOANALYSIS

We have come a long way since 1895 when Sigmund Freud planned his Project for a Scientific Psychology and then abandoned it for want of the necessary neurophysiological data. The neurophysiology that was not available to Freud in 1895 has become available within the last fifty years; and it is now possible to meet some of the demands of his Freud's ambition. Freud's pioneering insight into the nature of dreams was that they are produced by a concatenation of deep, primitive, emotional forces and by the meaningful associative integration of those forces with visual imagery and personal memory. However, the activation-synthesis hypothesis departs from Freud's theory in one fundamental respect. It holds that the dreaming brain, rather than disguising and concealing an unacceptable wish, is struggling to create coherence out of the disparate forces that are released by the brain in REM sleep, and that dreams are just what they appear to be: the auto-creative synthesis of emotion, instinct,

visual image, and memory bound together in a hyperassociative way. The driving impulses are neuronal activations, not unconscious wishes, and there is no disguise or censorship involved. As we shall see in later chapters of this book, it is a characteristic that they share with works of art that depict dreams or in various ways and contexts draw inspiration from them.

DREAMSTAGE: AN EXPERIMENTAL PORTRAIT OF THE SLEEP BRAIN

In 1975, when the activation-synthesis theory of dreaming was first taking shape, the opportunity arose to create an exhibition at the Carpenter Center for the Visual Arts at Harvard University which was called Dreamstage. The exhibit integrated artistic processes at the heart of the activation-synthesis theory in a real-time, on-line sleep laboratory. Dreamstage ran for five weeks in the spring of 1977. We placed a sleeper and a sleep lab in what we called a Dark Space, where the visitor could observe the sleeper and see sleep lab recordings of brain, muscle, eye, and heart physiology projected on the walls in the color-coded laser beams that the media artist, Paul Earls, programmed. These signals also generated sleep and dream music via a synthesizer.

In order to emphasize the dynamics of sleep behavior we projected all-night time-lapse photographs of sleepers by Theodore Spagna onto the white ceiling of the dark space. The periodic posture shifts that they revealed confirmed the transitions observed in the sleep laboratory of the transition from REM to non-REM sleep and vice versa. We also included the Swedish artist Ragnhild Reingardt's large-scale color field images of neurones, which were made by photographing histological slides of brain cells stained by two contrasting methods: the silver stain technique developed at the end of the nineteenth century by Camillo Golgi which yielded black spider-ike pictures of the branching neuronal connections on a golden field; and the aniline-luxol fast blue tint method devised by Kluver-Barrera, which differentiates between the neuronal nuclei and the nuclear chemicals that command the whole Darwinian life process, including our ability to sleep and dream. By means of these images we were able clearly to show that sleep and dreams are caused by an orderly internal brain activation process involving brain cells.

In what we called the Light Space (denoting daytime and waking consciousness), we exhibited images by scientists that conveyed their aesthetic response to the brain's function and structure. They included: India ink drawings by Ramon y Cajal and his student Rafael Lorente de No (see pages 41 and 190), some of which focus on the brainstem cells involved in generating REM and which may also create the convincing illusion of movement in dreams. We also showed drawings by Clinton Woolsey that help us to understand our conscious perception of our bodies by showing the allocation of brain space to maps of the body's surface. When these points are connected in a line drawing, they reveal a caricature of the body

Dreamscreen Bordeaux.

The anatomical and physiological imagery of Dreamstage was converted to the slide projection mode for the Bordeaux installation.

called Dreamscreen (1982). There was a live sleeper whose video image (see page 152) was projected on one screen together with his EEG pattern. In addition to brain anatomy and

physiology we also projected slides of Spagna's time-lapse photographic studies of human sleep and the dream drawings of the Engine Man. Visitors to the exhibit could hear

French language translations of the Engine Man's dream reports, which were synchronized with his drawings.

as seen by the brain as is shown on page 94.

In Bordeaux in 1982, we developed the neurophysiological and dream data by using lap-dissolve slide projection. We thus renamed the exhibition Dreamscreen. The shift meant converting hundreds of dream drawings and thousands of film-strip images of neurones in action to colored 2x2 slides. To animate the dream drawings by the Engine Man we used slides in each of which the dream movement's progress could by cumulated by adding color to the dashed lines by which the dreamer had indicated movement in his journal. To animate records of neuronal activity we color-coded sequences of up to fifty slides of the electrical activity of brain cells, EEG waves, and eye movements. The effect of viewing the sequences clearly showed the continuously modulated, auto-activation of the brain. Many of the scientific images in this book were generated for Dreamstage.

WHERE DO DREAMS COME FROM?

The scientific message of both Dream-stage and Dreamscreen was that dreaming occurs in sleep whenever the brain is sufficiently activated, gated, and modulated, and that the most favorable conditions for dreaming are, in increasing order:

Sleep onset when waking activation is residual, the input-output gates are rapidly closing, and modulation is rapidly subsiding; the dreams that occur at sleep onset are typically evanescent, and brief.

Late night NREM sleep when activation is rising but the gates are still closed and modulation is minimal; the dreams that occur then are typically short and often thought-like.

REM sleep when the general level of activation is as high as waking, the input-output gates are actively closed, modulation is most radically altered and internal stimuli are generated; the dreams that occur then are typically florid and sustained.

Of all these states, REM sleep provides the most ideal brain conditions for dreaming. Dreaming is seen as the inevitable mental accompaniment of altered brain physiology. There is no longer any reason to believe that unconscious wishes in the Freudian sense play an instigating role in oneirogenesis. Of course, once appropriately activated by physiology the dream can - and usually does - build upon current and past concerns, including frustrated desires and conflicts as it renders them in a unique scenario-like medium. But the instinctual emotional force of dreaming is more negative than positive. The anxiety and fear that are so common in dreams are a primary reflection of the limbic system activation that is part and parcel of REM sleep physiology, rather than a secondary reaction to a failed effort to disguise the unacceptable import of an unconscious wish.

WHY ARE DREAMS STRANGE?

One of the universal formal characteristics of dreams that we have emphasized in this chapter is bizarreness. The answer to the question why dreams are bizarre given by neurophysiology is again quite different from that of dynamic psychology. The activated, gated, and modulated brain generates an intrinsically heterogeneous mix of emotional turmoil (primarily anxiety). Sensory imagery of persons, places, and actions does its best to achieve a synthesis of these discontinuous and incongruous elements in keeping with the delusional belief by the dreamer that he or she is awake. But in the absence of both external time-space cues, and with working memory failing to maintain even an internally consistent set of orientational parameters, the semi-demented dreamer runs from place to place, vainly seeking to relieve confusion about missing airplane tickets, baggage, lecture notes and slides.

In the midst of this chaotic anguish the dreamer encounters friends and acquaintances that may be chimeras of one another. These collage-like dream characters may perform impressive acrobatics like flying, spinning, swirling, or whizzing across watery surfaces. Occasionally dreaming comes up with imaginative but not really practical inventions. The reason for the emotional outpourings, the visual imagery, the motoric exuberance, and the hyperassociative integration in dreaming is simply automatic off-line brain activation by the unrestrained, unbalanced cholinergic system. And the reason for the disorientation, lack of self-reflective awareness, and poor memory during and after dreaming is due to the subtraction from the brain of norepinephrine and serotonin.

In addition to its devastating effects upon neuronal integration and organizational direction, the demodulation may also contribute to dramatic shifts in regional activation. Hence the deactivation of the frontal cortex cannot help but make matters worse for working memory (already poor), directed thought (already practically nonexistent), and critical judgment (already markedly impaired). Dream bizarreness, like dream vision, is thus a primary integral consequence of distinctive brain physiology, not a function of active, elaborate disguise mechanisms designed to protect the enfeebled ego from unacceptable impulses. Processes by which Freud identified what he called the dream work such as symbol formation, displacement, and condensation are, to be sure, characteristics of dream synthesis; but these are cognitive stock-in-trade devices employed by the brain in all its states, and have no necessarily defensive, or transformative psychological function.

Where Do Dreams Go?

Unless awakenings occur and unless such awakenings are prompt and undisturbed by posture shifts, stretches, and yawns, somewhere between ninety-five and ninety-nine percent of all human dreaming is simply unremembered. Such recall as can be achieved is due to the rapid remodulation of the brain by norepinephrine and serotonin following the awakening. Then and only then, is detailed recall possible. And even then the recall is likely to be lost unless special efforts are made by the individual to capture the fugitive dream memory and record it permanently on audio tape or on paper. When such teaching aids are used, recall can be markedly increased. This further supports the activation-synthesis model of dream forgetting as a passive process that plays itself out willy-nilly unless it is actively combated.

The most favorable state for dream harvesting is REM sleep, especially in the early morning hours when awakening is easier, and recall more enduring. With the assistance of a bed partner accomplice (who can see the REMs and feel the muscle twitches), the incidence of recall of lengthy, detailed, bizarre dreams whose reports run to 1500-3000 words can be increased from near zero to ninety-five percent, especially if the awakening coincides with a vigorous flurry of REMs. And the longer into the REM period, the longer the report.

The inevitable final question must be: what do we do with dreams if they are remembered? Because so many of the personal meanings of dreams are transparent, we favor a do-it-yourself, take-a-look-in-the-mirror approach to interpreting dreams as is illustrated in Allan Hobson's recent book, *Thirteen Dreams That Freud Never Had*. Whatever we may say about the meaning of dreams, we stand in awe and fascination at their form. The point we are stressing in this book, and to which we return again, is that it is the formal structure of dreams that fulfills Freud's criteria for a science of dreaming that is "perspicacious and free from doubt." By constantly reminding us of our native talent for image generation, this view of dreaming, also links us to the creativity of artists throughout the ages.

English, 12th century, The Dream of Jacob, Lambeth Bible, Lambeth Palace Library, London.

According to the 28th chapter of *Genesis* the sleeping Jacob dreamed that a ladder reached up to heaven and that angels were ascending and descending it. Above the figure of Jacob asleep he is shown standing, anointing with oil the stones that have been his pillow. On the upper right is the sacrifice of Isaac, and at the top of the ladder, holding a scroll, is God the Father.

Lighter than Air

Winged Gods, Angels, and Other Weightless Dream Agents

> *The dream departed at his word, descending*
> *swift as wind to where the long ships lay,*
> *And sought the son of Atreus. In his hut*
> *He found him sleeping, drifted all about*
> *with balm of slumber. At the marshall's pillow*
> *standing still, the dream took shape*
> *as Neleus' son, old Nestor. Agamemnon*
> *deferred to Nestor most, of all his peers;*
> *so in his guise the dream spoke to the dreamer.*

Homer, *The Iliad*

Throughout classical antiquity and well into the Renaissance, popular belief attributed states of consciousness such as sleep and dreams to spirits from other worlds. Dreams, which we now know to arise from automatic functions of the brain in sleep, were thought to be omens or messages brought to men by winged gods. The lightness and swiftness of the winged bearers of dreams accounted for their ubiquity and evanescence. The Greeks never spoke of "having" a dream, but of "seeing" one.

In this chapter we examine the theories that dreams originated in external agencies which flourished during classical antiquity and the Middle Ages. We shall attempt to show that these theories accomplished two important goals: to explain where dreams came from and what they meant. Although the winged gods/angels paradigm was dominant throughout the first millennium of Western civilization, there were already

strong hints of the paradigm shift to come. Those who questioned the theory of an external, divine agency to account for dreaming included Aristotle, Cicero, and Lucretius, who were also critical of interpretations based upon the assumptions of divine inspiration.

By taking this position contrary to popular belief, these thinkers averted the otherwise insurmountable obstacle posed by the contrast between the apparent interpretability of some dreams and the arrant nonsense of others. This dilemma led even many of the adherents of the external agency theory to compromise and to entertain the notion of two mechanisms, one internal, producing dreams of no significance, the other external, bringing dreams of prophetic import.

Our point is that even in the earliest, pre-Socratic dream theories of classical antiquity (ca.400 BC) that have come down to us, there is a nascent reliance on physiology in accounting for oneiric phenomena. By enlarg-

Head of Hypnos, Greek, 3rd century BC, British Museum, London.

The winged god Hypnos, the son of Morpheus, the god of sleep, was the principal bearer of dreams in Greek mythology. Upon reaching his destination after transversing the night, he removed his wings and transformed himself into a human shadow.

ing upon the importance of physiology, modern dream theory, not surprisingly, is encountering extreme resistance from contemporary schools of thought still dedicated to psychological variants of the prophetic tradition. While the balance may have shifted from external to internal agency theories, and the interpretation of dreams from the prophetic and metaphoric to the literal and the here-and-now, powerful vestiges of this conflict are still with us. Our discussion of selected classical, post-classical, and medieval texts is focused on the continuing dilemma posed by the scientific untenability of claims, whether ancient or modern, to dream interpretation.

THE WINGED GODS OF GREECE AND ROME

In Greek mythology the principal bearer of dreams to men was the winged god Hypnos, the son of Morpheus, the god of sleep, who was himself the son of Nyx (Night) and the brother of Thanatos (Death). In a drawing by the German neo-classical artist Asmus Jacob Carstens of *Night with her Children Sleep and Death* the seated goddess, Night, is spreading out her veil. Between her knees is Death holding a lowered torch. Sleep is leaning on Night's left thigh, holding poppy seed capsules. According to Ovid,

Skull X-Ray with EEG.

The human brain is contained within a bony box, the skull, which can be visualized by X-Ray photographic imagery.

The electrical activity of the brain is visualized by electroencephalographic tracing (green lines). These images were drawn from the Dreamstage Exhibit (1977-1982).

Brain electrical activity, like an angel, is lighter than air. Dreaming can occur in many people at the same time because each sleeper electrically activates his or her brain periodically during sleep. There is no longer a need to attribute dreaming to outside forces.

John Flaxman, *The Dream of Penelope, ca. 1790.*

In Greek mythology the gods could assume human form as the bearers of dreams. Flaxman's engraving illustrates an episode in Book IV of the *Odyssey* in which Athena takes the form of Penelope's sister Iphthime to bring a dream to Penelope reassuring her about the fate of her son Telemachus.

Sleep and his sons resided in a

deep recess within a hollow mountain. Clouds of vapor breathe forth from the earth, and dark twilight shadows. Around on all sides lie empty dream-shapes, mimicking many forms.

It was the task of Hypnos to assume the forms of men and appear to them in dreams. With his wings he was able swiftly and silently to traverse the darkness. Upon reaching his destination, he removed his wings and transformed himself into a human shadow. No other, Ovid wrote,

is more skilled than he in representing the gait, the features, and the speech of men; the clothing also and the accustomed words of each he represents.

The problems that the Hypnos hypothesis was designed to resolve include (1) the ubiquity of dreams in sleep, requiring extreme speed if the agency was external, (2) the invisibility of the agent, and, most important, (3) the versimilitude of dream characters. The modern alternative is a universal autonomous brain activation process which creates lifelike images from the inside out.

The Olympian gods too could assume human form and bring dreams to men. In Book IV of the *Odyssey* Athena takes on the figure of a dream in the form of Penelope's sister Iphthime, and sends the dream to Penelope to reassure her about the fate of her son Telemachus, the subject of one of seven engravings by John Flaxman illustrating the translation of the *Odyssey* by Alexander Pope.

During the Hellenistic period the Greek

god of love Eros, described by Plato in the *Symposium* as having the "power to provide all virtue and happiness for men whether living or dead," also became the bearer of sleep, dreams, and death. In the Roman copy of a Hellenistic original in the Uffizi (shown on page 42) he is shown as a playful winged Cupid overcome by sleep. In his right hand is the stem of two capsules of poppy seeds, proof that the ancients were familiar with this plant's opiate properties. The Greek physician Dioscorides (1st century AD) wrote in his *De Materia Medica*, the foremost textbook on pharmacology until well into the Middle Ages, that the opium obtained from poppy was used to make sleeping potions, indicating awareness of a chemical mechanism by which the plant extract directly influenced the brain of sleepers.

The association of Eros with sleep, dreams and death appears to go back to Hesiod's *Theogony* (c.700 BC), where he is described as the god who "loosens the limbs and damages the mind." Because his power to arouse love and desire also brings peril, the lyric poets of the 7th and 6th centuries BC portrayed him as cunning and cruel, appearing suddenly like the wind and shaking or smiting his victims. We should also keep in mind the kinship in Greek mythology between Hypnos (dreams), Morpheus (sleep) and Thanatos (death), by which the ancient world explained the fact that sleep and dreams are a kind of death insofar as they deprive us of our conscious awareness and self-reflection, and plunge us into an unkown unpredictable realm in which we are no longer masters of our fate. In the course of the solilo-

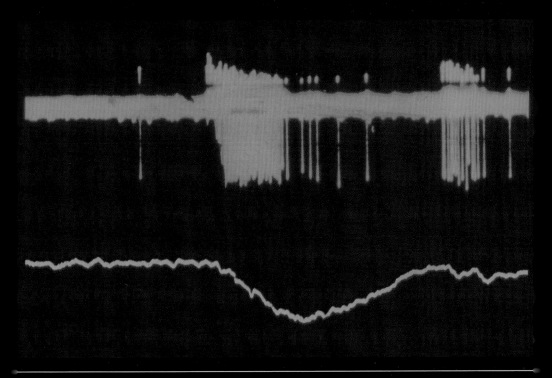

Eye Movement Cell.

When cells of the pontine reticular fire bursts of action potentials, the eyes are caused to move. This process is useful in waking as eye movement is essential to vision. The same process may also contribute to dream vision. When the eyes move in the absence of external (light) input, it is clear that the upper brain receives detailed information about brain stem initiated eye movement. Visual imagery, it can be concluded, is an internally generated aspect of consciousness.

quy in which Hamlet poses the question "To be or not to be," he is brought up short by the thought:

To die, to sleep;
To sleep, perchance to dream - ay, there's the rub:
For in that sleep of death what dreams may come,
When we have shuffled off this mortal coil,
Must give us pause -

ARTEMIDORUS AND DREAM INTERPRETATION

Despite the prevalent and popular belief in the ancient world that dreams were brought to men by winged gods, not all classical and late-antique writers subscribed to the idea that dreams were divinely sent messages. Artemidorus of Ephesus, the author of the *Oneirocritica*, a manual of dreams assembled at the end of the 2nd century, cautiously avoided the question. He was a recorder and compiler, not a philosopher. At the beginning of his dream book he acknowledged that

I do not inquire, like Aristotle, whether the cause of our dreaming is outside of us and comes from the gods or whether it is motivated by something within.

But whatever its origin, every dream in the *Oneirocritica* had a hidden meaning - Freud was to call it the dream's "latent content" - that required interpretation. Artemidorus treated all dreams with clinical, practical matter-of-factness. There was nothing a person could dream that did not predict something:

If a debtor dreams that any of his teeth fall out, regardless of their type, it signifies that he will pay off his debt. If all the teeth fall out together, it signifies, in the case of people who are healthy, free, and who are not merchants, that their house will be deserted by everyone alike. If someone loses a single tooth, he will pay off his debt to one person, or to many people at once.

Belief in the prophetic efficacy of dreams had existed in the Mediterranean region long before Artemidorus' time. According to a text recently discovered at the Egyptian village of Deir el-Medina (circa 1070 BC), dreaming of copulating with a woman is a bad omen, while dreaming of mating with a cow is a good sign, foretelling a happy day in the house. The patent absurdity of such amusing interpretations, and that fact that they have stood the test of time, are testimony to our preference for a scientifically groundless explanation of bizarre mental activity to the suggestion that there may be none, or none other than chaotic brain activity in sleep. Modern dream lexicons have nothing to fear in comparison with Artemidorus. They are equally authoritarian and arbitrary. And they are equally popular.

Although most dreams in the Oneirocritica refer to future events, their significance must be read - as in Freud's *Interpretation of Dreams* - in the context of the dreamer's personal history. Like Freud, Artemidorus emphasized the principle of association - the ideas that dream images evoke in consciousness. But whereas Freud was interested in the associations of the dreamer, Artemidorus was concerned with the associations evoked by the dream image in the mind of the interpreter. The attribution by Artemidorus of specific prophetic meaning to dreams has never lost its spell. It was revived in Byzantine dream books, most notably in the *Book of Dreams* by Nicephorus, patriarch of Constantinople from 806 to 815; and following the translation of the *Oneirocritica* into European Languages in the Renaissance, Artemidorus' method of decoding the messages of dreams became a staple of popular dream books into our own time.

THE ORIGIN OF DREAMS

The tension between divine and human explanations of dreams reflected in Artemidorus' ambivalence about their origin appears repeatedly in the writings of classical and late-antique authors. The earliest rational explanation of dreams in the ancient world is found among the fragments of the pre-Socratic philosopher Heraclitus (450-375 BC), who regarded dreams as the ordinary accompaniments of sleep, and sleeping as a state of isolation from the world and one another:

The world of the waking is one and shared, but the sleeping turn aside each into his private world.

According to Heraclitus, the onset of sleep (Morpheus), when we have lost contact with the light of day, is a kind of death (Thanatos):

A man strikes a light for himself in the night, when his sight is quenched. Living, he touches the dead in his sleep; waking, he touches the sleeper.

We compensate for the fact that our sight is shut down at nightfall by lighting a lamp, and thus, sleeping, "touch" the realm of the dead. When we awake, we return to the daytime state, but are now "in touch" with our descent into the dream world. Marcel Proust described the journey of the sleeping soul into the underworld of dreams in virtually identical terms in a passage in *À la récherche du temps perdu*:

Suddenly I was asleep, I had fallen into that deep slumber in which are opened to us...the transmigration of the soul, the evoking of the dead... all those mysteries which we imagine ourselves not to know and into which we are in reality initiated almost every night.

The analogy to darkness and to death, a virtual shutting down of the mind - which the Greeks explained by the blood relationship between Hypnos, Morpheus, and Thanatos - is understandable and still valid with respect to sleep onset and to early night NREM sleep when global brain activation falls to very low levels. The analogy is less apt for dreams, since dreams imply the reactivation of the brain that we now know regularly punctuates sleep and becomes increasingly intense as the night goes on.

A PLATONIC DIALOGUE

Plato attributed dreams to the "inner motions" of the soul which, as neuroscience has confirmed, arise spontaneously while we are asleep. When our eyelids are shut, he wrote in the *Timaeus*, these inner motions are at rest and

quiet ensues; and when this quiet has become intense there falls upon us a sleep that is well-nigh dreamless; but when some greater motions are still left behind, such and so great are the images they produce, which images are copied within and are remembered by the sleepers when they awake out of the dream.

Plato's insight is keen as far as it goes. There is a residual level of activation which accounts for dreams at sleep onset and for the dreams that accompany non-REM sleep. But the question arises: can that be all? Or don't we have to postulate an additional activation process arising in the brain itself to account for the prolonged, intense, and strikingly bizarre dreams we have in the early morning? Plato was clearly unaware of this phenomenological distinction because he did not make direct observations or perform experiments.

Dreamstage sleeper.

In the full view of an audience that over five weeks ran to 10.000 people, the Dreamstage subject slept naturally and deeply while his brain activity was recorded ad displayed on the walls of the exhibit.

The secret of this surprising fact was to emphasize that the sleeper's job was to stay awake when not in the exhibit. The silver lamé bed cover (which conceals and reveals the sleeper's body) was designed by Clara Wainwright.

The Rationalism of Aristotle, Cicero, and Lucretius

Aristotle (384-322 BC) was more biologically sophisticated than Plato, but he too eschewed experimentation. He denied the divine origin of dreams on two grounds: the observation of animals when they are asleep shows that they also dream; and it is unreasonable to reconcile the notion that dreams come from God with the fact that He sends them not to the best and wisest, but to people at random. It is difficult to imagine how this argument could survive the Christian imputation of democratic fairness to God; but neuroscience has shown, on other grounds, that the universality of dreaming in humans and other animals beto-

kens an internal agent. Dreaming for Aristotle is "an activity of the faculty of sense-perception, but belongs to this faculty imaginatively." By "imaginatively" he meant that

even when the external object of perception has departed, the impressions it has made persist, and are themselves objects of perception. [Therefore] movements based upon sensory impressions, whether the latter are derived from external objects or from causes within the body, are present not only when persons are awake, but also occur when sleep has come upon them.

Like Plato, Aristotle had trouble going beyond the idea of residual activation; but he was close to the mark in his emphasis on sensory-motor mechanisms. He thus defined "the dream proper" as "an image based on the movement of sense impression when it occurs in sleep." Because hallucinations, illusions, and fantasies have much in common with dreams, he concluded that although this might indicate that they share a common origin,

dreams are not sent by God, nor are they designed for this purpose. They have a mysterious aspect, however, for nature is mysterious, though not divine.

Both Cicero (106-43 BC) and Lucretius (99-55 BC) considered dreams to be natural occurrences no more and no less than the mental operations and sensations while we are awake. Cicero, the most rational of ancient philosophers, distinguished the direct, clear dream (*visio*) from the veiled, allegorical one (*somnium*), but put no faith in either, because

if God is not the creator of dreams; if there is no connection between them and the laws of nature; and finally, if, by means of observation no art of divining can be found in them, it follows that absolutely no reliance can be placed in dreams.

In *De rerum natura* Lucretius described dreaming in terms not inconsistent with the formal characteristics of dreams - hallucination, delusion, bizarreness, incongruity, and amnesia - that we have defined in this book:

When sleep has fast bound our limbs with sweet drowsiness, and our whole body lies in profound quiet, yet we seem to ourselves then to be awake and to move our limbs, and in the blind darkness of night we think that we see the sun and the light of day, and we seem to exchange our narrow room for the sky and sea, rivers and mountains, and traverse plains afoot, and to hear sounds though the stern silence of night reigns everywhere, and to utter speech while saying nothing. We see in marvelous fashion many things

besides of this kind, so that things are held to be seen which have not been seen by our senses... It sometimes happens again, that the image that follows up is not of the same kind, but what was before a woman seems to be changed into a man in our grasp; or that different shapes and ages follow; but sleep and oblivion see to it that we do not wonder.

The question arises why empirically based observations such as Lucretius' were so rare, and why it took so long to make other observations of a formal kind regarding dreaming. The answer can only be that we are still under the spell of classical humanism and medieval scholasticism. We continue to assume that an unseen hand guides our destiny, and that the motives of this prime mover can be discovered through the decoding of dream content.

Lucretius also noticed the eye movements at the onset of sleep and inferred a relationship to dreaming, though neither he nor anyone else quite grasped the significance of this observation until 1953, when Aserinsky and Kleitman discovered that rapid eye movement (or REM) sleep was the optimal physical basis of dreaming.

GALEN AND THE HUMORAL THEORY OF DREAMING

Two centuries after Cicero and Lucretius, Artemidorus listed two dream theories current at his time: first, the view promoted by Lucretius and other Epicurean writers that they are nothing more than a continuation of the day's activities (what Freud called "the day's residue"), aimed at undermining the popular belief that dreams are sent by the gods; and second, the theory of Hippocrates (460-377 BC) and Galen (129-199 AD) that dreams are the result of indigestion, intoxication, or an imbalance in the humors, and provide physicians with clues as to the nature of physical disorders. A dream, Galen wrote in his treatise *On Diagnosis Through Dreams*,

indicates to us the condition of the body. If anyone should see a fire in his dreams he is troubled by too much yellow bile; if he should see smoke, or a misty darkness or profound shadows, then by black bile.

Galen's belief in the humoral theory of the determination of dream content and in the usefulness of dream content in the diagnosis of bodily illness, even if those assumptions have significantly changed, can be discerned in our own hypotheses. In the context of neurobiology, Galen's bodily humors become brain modulators. Dreaming occurs when aminergic neuromodulation decreases and cholinergic neuromodulation remains high or rises. This is nothing more - or less - than a humoral theory of dreaming. The difference - and it is a very significant difference - between it and Galen's theory is that ours has an empirical rather than a theoretical origin.

With respect to the use of dream content in diagnosis, we are also followers of Galen when we argue that dreaming, being humorally determined, provides a window for understanding mental illness. We call the illnesses in question mental because we cannot yet easily see how they could be bodily. Yet the modern dream theory facilitates this formulation by making plausible the idea that psychoses are caused by humoral imbalances in the brain. Moreover, the kind of mental content observed in dreamers is beginning to suggest specific kinds of humoral imbalance. For example, the auditory hallucinations and paranoia of schizophrenia denote dopamine-glutamate imbalance, while the visual hallucinations, disorientation, confabulations, and memory loss of organic delirium suggest aminergic-cholinergic imbalance. The interested reader will find a detailed exposition of these arguments in *The Dream Drugstore* published by MIT Press in 2001.

TRUE AND FALSE DREAMS

Dream origin theories during the 4th and 5th centuries tended to occupy a middle ground between the human and the divine. For the Neo-Platonist Iamblichus (250-330) both divine and human dreams are possible, though they signify different things. Divine dreams, which emanate from God and allow the soul to transcend its mortal condition, are true. Human dreams, which arise from within, whether "excited by the soul, by some of our conceptions, by the imagination, or by daily cares," are fallible, "sometimes true and sometimes false."

The distinction between true and false dreams is not incompatible with the evidence of neuroscience that the dreaming brain is prone to hyperassociate in a meaningful as well as a nonsensical manner, depending on the altered state of its physiology and chemistry. The differentiation between true and false dreams was one of the cornerstones of dream theories from antiquity to the Renaissance. Its origin is in Homer. In Book XIX of the *Odyssey* Penelope asks the disguised Odysseus to interpret a dream in which an eagle, speaking in Odysseus' voice, predicted that he will return to her and bring death to the suitors. Odysseus tells her that the dream will come true. But

Penelope shook her head and answered:
"Friend, many and many a dream
is mere confusion,
a cobweb of no consequence at all.
Two gates for ghostly dreams there are: one gateway
of honest horn, and one of ivory.
Issuing by the ivory gates are dreams
of glimmering illusions, fantasies,
but those that come through solid polished horn
may be borne out, if mortals only know them.
I doubt it came by horn, my fearful dream -
too good to be true, that, for my son and me."

The 2nd-century Greek satirist Lucian was, like Iamblichus a century later, of two minds

French, 12th century, The Dream of the Magi, Saint-Lazare, Autun.

The carving on the Romanesque capital at Autun illustrates the story in the Gospel of St. Matthew that after the three magi had paid homage to the new-born Christ, God warned them in a dream not to return to King Herod but to take another route back to their own country.

about the origin and significance of dreams. At the beginning of his essay on dreams Lucian announced that "a vision in a dream has come to me in the starry night," quoting Agamemnon's response to the dream sent to him by Zeus in Book II of the *Iliad*. Yet after having recounted his dream, Lucian thought it possible that "it was due, I suppose, to my agitation." If, he went on to say, the dream was of divine origin, it deserves a receptive audience; if, on other hand, it was psychologically motivated, it prompts the audience's derision. One is a meaningful revelation, the other is meaningless.

Macrobius' Commentary on the "Dream of Scipio"

Artemidorus too made a distinction between the dream which has allegorical meaning and can foretell the future (somnium), and the insomnium, which arises from the state of the dreamer's body and mind and is without significance. In this as well as in other respects the *Oneirocritica* was the point of departure for the Commentary on Cicero's *Dream of Scipio* by the 5th-century Roman writer Macrobius, the most important dream book of late antiquity whose influence reached as far as the sixteenth century. Macrobius' commentary on the *Dream of Scipio* is the culmination of the struggle from the time of Homer onward to decide what to value and interpret, and what to devalue and cast aside. It is our deep conviction that to make this distinction consistently and objectively is not only difficult but impossible, and that for this reason all interpretative schemata will continue to fail the test of scientific validity. We are also aware of the fact that the confounding of phenomenology (what can be objectively observed) with interpretability (the subjective quest for verbal formulations of what observed data might mean) continues to hinder dream science - and not only dream science - down to our own day.

Macrobius distinguished between four principal categories of dreams: visio, somnium, insomnium, and phantasma. The definition of the *visio* and the *somnium*, both of which are prophetic, goes back to Cicero. The *visio* is the direct, clear vision. It is comprehensible because what the visionary sees will come to pass. The somnium is the allegorical dream which

conceals strange shapes and veils with ambiguity the true meaning of the information being offered and requires an interpretation in order to be understood.

The *insomnium*, or nightmare, and the phantasma, or apparition,

are not worth interpreting since they have no prophetic significance. Nightmares may be caused by mental or physical distress, or anxiety about the future. They flee when the dreamer awakes and vanish into thin air. Thus the name insomnium was given, not because such dreams occur in sleep, but because they are noteworthy only during their course, and afterwards have no importance or meaning. The apparition comes upon one in the moment between wakefulness and slumber. In this drowsy condition the dreamer thinks he is still fully awake and imagines he sees specters rushing at him or wandering vaguely about, differing from natural creatures in size and shape, and hosts of diverse things, either delightful or disturbing. The two types of dreams just described are of no assistance in foretelling the future; but by means of the other two we are gifted with the powers of divination.

Throughout the Middle Ages and the Renaissance the *visio* and the *somnium* were considered true, the *insomnium* and the phantasma false. For the sake of convenience the Middle Ages reduced Macrobius' four categories to three. Because medieval writers spoke of visions and dreams interchangeably, the *visio* and the *somnium* were distilled into the *somnium coeleste*. The *insomnium*, or nightmare,

...ieval Pilgrim.

...ieval Pilgrim ...head through

the dome-like edge of the cosmos and listens to the music of the spheres. The infinite and chaotic nature

of outer (and inner) space could not be comprehended as chance events by anyone until the

modern, Post-Dar... era.

...e the *somnium animale*, and the *phantas-* ...apparition, was renamed the *somnium* ...e. The *somnium coeleste*, whether it took ...n of a direct vision or of a veiled dream ...ng interpretation, was prophetic and of ...l origin. The *somnium animale* and the ...n *naturale*, whose sources were located ...the dreamer's mind and body, came ...the province of medieval medicine. ...ing to the Arab physician and philoso- ...vicenna (980-1037), the *somnium ani-* ...brings from great anxiety in the waking ...while the *somnium naturale*, or appari- ...a symptom of bodily illness, caused by ...balance of the humors. Prophetic ...on the other hand, "result from a ...action of angelic intelligences on the ...sleep, acting upon the imagination."

In the light of modern dream scien... visio, or prophetic dream vision, could... the elusive prophetic insights that are g... ed when sleepers are preoccupied durin... ing consciousness with uncertainty and... about the future. The evidence sugges... such preoccupations prime the brain to... orate with the intensified emotions, es... fear and elation, automatically genera... sleep. Dreams can and do reflect the dr... concern about the future, and they may... times coincide with a specific outcome; b... cannot be taken as scientific evidence fo... than chance predictions of the future.

The *somnium*, or allegorical dream,... duced by a REM process that drives th... thetic and creative circuits of the brain... erate metaphors, symbols, and confab...

mystification. In other words, dreaming may be the mental state par excellence for hyperassociative processing; but that should not be construed as a warrant for interpretability. Indeed, if the approach to interpretation is reductive, it would seem more likely to lead to error. The *insomnium*, or nightmare, is caused by intense activation of the limbic brain in sleep that triggers rapid heart action, respiratory irregularity, and increased blood pressure. These effects can occur in bad dreams during REM sleep, or as post-traumatic flashbacks during non-REM sleep. The *phantasma*, or apparition, alludes to the evocation arising from the activation of the limbic system in REM sleep of hypnagogic hallucinations and associated negative emotions. Here again, the occurrence of nightmares and hypnagogic phenomena attest more to the potent connections between emotional and cognitive activation in sleep than they provide clues to reducing distress via catharsis.

Dreaming in the Middle Ages

In Christian thought prophetic dreams were a meeting place of the present and eternity, the vehicle for the union of the dreamer with the divine, and an intermediary between matter and spirit. The idea that matter and spirit, or body and mind, are separate entities persisted into modern times. Even the French philosopher René Descartes (1596-1650), who understood the reality of the physical brain, could not imagine its relationship to mental experience. It is only within the last half-century that modern neuroscience has demonstrated the unifying interdependence of brain and mind.

The Christian Middle Ages translated the pagan winged gods into angels, bearers of what Avicenna called "angelic intelligences," who mediated between the realm of God and the realm of man, bringing portents or visions

to enlightened dreamers. A frequently illustrated visionary subject of Christian art, from the 12th century to the period of Romanticism, is the account in chapter 28 of Genesis of the dream of Jacob, which from the Middle Ages onward was interpreted as symbolizing the ascent of the soul to heaven. Having received his father Isaac's blessing, Jacob went to Mesopotamia, to his mother Rebecca's brother Laban. On the way he

lighted upon a certain place and tarried there all night, because the sun was set; and he took the stones of that place, and put them for his pillows, and lay down in that place to sleep. And he dreamed, and behold a ladder was set up on the earth, and the top of it reached to heaven: and behold the angels of the Lord ascending and descending on it.

The anonymous English illuminator of *The Dream of Jacob* in a twelfth-century bible in the Lambeth Palace Library has placed the ladder with five ascending angels diagonally across the page, with the dreaming Jacob at the lower left. (On the right of the page is the Sacrifice of Isaac, which medieval biblical commentators interpreted as a symbolic prefiguration of the sacrifice of Christ. Above the sleeping Jacob he is shown standing, awake after his dream and anointing with oil the stones that were his pillow. At the top of the God the Father holds a scroll with the inscription "I am God").

The ladder is an obvious device for getting from one level to another and back. Higher levels can thereby be accessed by sleepers who ascend dream ladders; and the agents of transformations can also descend from higher realms imparting messages to dreamers. In modern sleep research the ladder is replaced by a graph that shows brain activation initially to fall to relative unconsciousness and oblivion, and later to rise again, step by step, to a level near that of waking where vivid dreaming can ensue.

The preferred recipients of dreams in medieval art were Old Testament patriarchs, saints, and rulers, including the Three Magi. A capital in the French Romanesque cathedral at Autun illustrates the account in the Gospel of St. Matthew that after the Magi had paid homage to the new-born Christ, God commanded them in a dream not to return to Herod, "and they took another route back to their country." The medieval carver has shown the angel who is the bearer of God's command touching the hand of one of the sleeping kings, and pointing to the star they should follow on their way home. The fact that the three kings appear to have their eyes open classifies the dream as Macrobius' visio, the direct, clear vision, suggesting that the Magi are in fact seeing the angelic messenger and receiving the message that the angel brings them from on high.

On the Threshold of the Renaissance

One of the subjects of the frescoes of the life of St. Francis in the Upper Church of San Francesco at Assisi is *The vision of St. Francis* in which an angel, pointing to a magnificent palace decked with banners, bids the saint and his followers become soldiers of Christ. Under the fresco is the following inscription:

On the following night, when Saint Francis had dropped off to sleep, he saw a large and splendid place adorned with martial banners of the sign of the Cross of Christ; and when he asked whose they were, a celestial voice answered him that they were all his and his soldiers'.

The fact that the artist has rendered the palace to which the angel is pointing - a curious mixture of classical and Gothic styles - in perspective, as a structure that could actually be built, anticipates the humanistic and scientific interests of the Renaissance in the physical reality of both dreams and their pictorial representation. By the middle of the 15th century these interests had advanced to the point that in Piero della Francesca's fresco of the *Dream of Constantine* in the choir of San Francesco in Arezzo, the emperor's vision is shown as if it were taking place in front of our eyes. Asleep in his tent the night before his battle at the Milvian bridge against Maxentius, Constantine has a dream in which an angel announces the prophecy that he will prevail by the sign of the cross. Piero's realism extends to the fact that he has staged the dream at night, and shown the angel bringing the prophetic message as we would see him, in foreshortening from the back.

Anticipations of Modern Dream Science

The last, most prescient writer of the ancient world who considered dreams a natural phenomena susceptible to a purely psycho-physiological explanation was the 4th-century Greek theologian Gregory of Nyssa. In his *On the Making of Man* (380) Gregory attributed dreaming to the fact that in sleep the senses and the intellect are inactive. From this observation he drew the conclusion that dreams are motivated by the passions, which while we are awake must be held in check by the intellect if man is not to fall into sin; but because in sleep the intellect ceases to be vigilant, our passions find expression in dreams.

Essentially the same point was made at the end of the 18th century by Francisco Goya's etching *El sueño de la razon produce monstruos* (The Sleep of Reason Produces Monsters). Under a preparatory drawing for the etching Goya wrote:

The author dreaming. His only intention is to banish harmful common beliefs and to perpetuate

Dream Drawings.

In dreams, it is possible to fly, to fall or to hang perilously in space. In the case of the Smithsonian Insect Specialist, such involuntary dream situations as hanging from railway tracks and kneeling on a flying carpet, are fraught with anxiety. When dream flying is induced by pre-sleep autosuggestion, it can be quite pleasurable however. Instead of dreams being brought by winged creature dreamers have the intrinsic capacity to simulate flight.

with this work of caprichos the sound testimony of truth.

Goya's etching is not directed against reason, but implies that the monsters of "harmful common beliefs" that come to the fore in dreams when reason is asleep can be defeated - that "the sound testimony of truth" can prevail - if reason is "vigilant."

Gregory of Nyssa, had a view of the motivation of dreams that anticipates not only Goya, but also Freud and modern dream science. Like the neuroscientist in his laboratory, Gregory was more interested in the structure of dreams and in how dreams work than in dream content and its interpretation. And his conclusion that dreams are motivated by the passions when they are not checked by the intellect precedes by a millennium-and-a-half Freud's hypotheses that when we are asleep the intellect - Freud called it the ego - abandons its supremacy, and material the ego has censored and relegated to the unconscious during waking consciousness is symbolically expressed in dreams.

From the point of view of modern dream science the most remarkable aspect of Gregory's model of the interaction of volition and passion is its anticipation of the discovery that the seat of volition in the frontal lobe of the brain is in dynamic interaction with the seat of emotion in the limbic lobe. That interaction is such that in normal dreaming, compared to waking, the frontal volitional system is deactivated while the limbic emotional center is activated. Thus in dreams we are incapable of exercising volitional control over our dreaming selves, and our emotions come to dominate the mind.

For this to occur we need no winged gods, no angels, and no ladder. A healthy brain equipped with its own intrinsic capacity to change its activation level, open and close its input-output gates, and to change its neuromodulatory ratios is all that is required. These capacities, in turn, regulate the automatic activation and deactivation of the neuronal ensembles in specific regions of the brain controlling reason and passion. The way they operate is, by any account, nothing short of wondrous. For those who still wish to posit external agencies such as astrological configurations, and who delight in the decoding of symbols, we acknowledge that no scientific findings yet disprove such schemes. However, by providing a simpler and more securely founded model, modern dream science relieves competing thought systems of the responsibility for substantiating their authority.

It seems to us no accident that the lasting significance of late-antique thinkers, particularly of Gregory of Nyssa, derives from emphasis upon the universal form of dreaming and related mental states. Perhaps we will one day know enough to put hypotheses of content analyses to scientific tests. But that day has not come. When it does, we suspect that our formal approach may well have cleared up most of the mystery of dreaming.

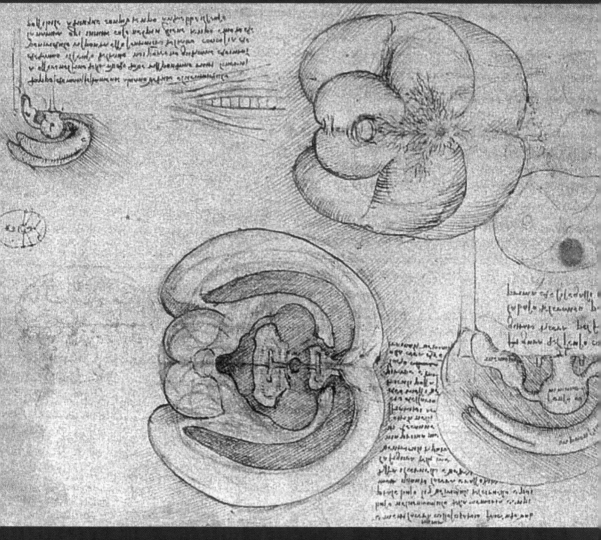

Leonardo's Brain.

The great Italian Renaissance artist-scientist, Leonardo daVinci, observed- and drew – the brain as well as other parts of human anatomy. In these sketches, he depicts the fluid-filled cavities, called ventricles, which contain the spinal fluid that helps to cushion the brain and may serve as internal canals for the transport of chemicals from one region to another. During the Renaissance, the physical basis of phenomena previously ascribed to extracorporeal agencies was sought – and found – at the level of bodily mechanisms.

Such Stuff As Dreams Are Made On

The Phisical Reality of Sleep and Dreams

Dreams are but interludes, which fancy makes,
When monarch reason sleeps, this mimic wakes;
Compounds a medley of disjointed things,
A mob of cobblers, and a court of kings.

John Dryden, *The Cock and the Fox (1700)*

One of the major contributions to knowledge of the new science of dreaming is the light that the processes by which the brain generates dreams sheds on the nature of consciousness. Rather than viewing dreaming as the path to the unconscious, as Freud did, the new science of dreaming considers dreaming as an altered state of consciousness whose distinctive features reflect changes in the brain systems controlling consciousness as a whole. The intuition of a relationship between dreaming, the brain, and consciousness goes back to the Renaissance; and it stimulated the investigation of the physiological and psychological links between dreams and the brain by Renaissance humanists, philosophers, and artists. What was missing was observational data. Little by little, with the growth during the Renaissance of naturalistic observation, including dissection of the human body, such data began to be collected.

One of the most telling examples of the Renaissance interest in the observation and representation of sleep and of the intermediary stages between waking and sleeping is Michelangelo's four reclining figures of the Times of Day on the sarcophagi of Giuliano and Lorenzo de' Medici in the Medici Chapel of San Lorenzo in Florence. The source for Michelangelo's choice of the Times of Day would seem to have been Dante's *Convivio*, a handbook in verse of universal knowledge, in which the poet describes life as an arc that rises and falls and has four segments: the four ages of man, the four seasons, and the four times of day. Michelangelo has represented the arc of life in the form of the cycle of Night (sleep) and Day (waking) (under the statue of Giuliano) and of the intermediary stages of Dawn and Dusk (under the statue of Lorenzo). The sculptures anticipate the photographs of Theodore Spagna recording sleep and the stages between sleeping and waking. In the middle of the 16th century Giorgio Vasari wrote of Michelangelo's figure of Night that "in this statue Michelangelo expressed the very essence of sleep."

Michelangelo, Tomb of Giuliano de' Medici, ca.1525-1530, Medici Chapel, San Lorenzo, Florence.

The reclining figures on this tomb and on the tomb of Lorenzo de'Medici represent the four times of day in terms of the cycle of sleep (*Night*) and waking (*Day*) on the tomb of Giuliano, and the stages between them, *Dawn* and *Dusk*, on the tomb of Lorenzo. As such, they are unique anticipations of the time-lapse photographs of sleep, waking, and the stages in between, by Theodore Spagna.

Michelangelo, Tomb of Lorenzo de' Medici, ca.1525-1530, Medici Chapel, San Lorenzo, Florence.

While artists anticipated the modern scientific interest in the direct observation of sleep, scholars located the source of consciousness in the fluid-filled cavities, or ventricles, and the discrete parts of the brain, such as the pineal gland which René Descartes, a century-and-a-half later, regarded as the seat of the soul. Among Leonardo da Vinci's studies of the anatomy of the human body are drawings of the skull and of its mysterious content, the brain, injected to demonstrate the shape of the cerebral ventricles.

The Freedom of the Soul in Dreams

From the fact that during sleep the senses and the intellect are inactive, Renaissance writers drew a different conclusion from Gregory of Nyssa. Gregory inferred from this that when the intellect does not hold the passions in check, they are given free rein to find expression in dreams. Renaissance philosophers concluded that because when we are asleep the senses and the intellect receive no messages from the outside world, the soul, left to its own devices, operates in terms of its own "pure conceptions" (puris rationibus). This idea resonates with the modern scientific hypothesis that, in dreaming, consciousness reveals its own intrinsic capacities, including visualization, belief construction, the processing of associations, and the generation of salient emotion. It does this because the self-activated brain is "off-line" in REM sleep, deprived of its inputs and outputs, as Renaissance thinkers surmised. What they did not suspect was that the dreaming brain is also chemically altered.

In the humanistic and scientific climate of the Renaissance the autonomy of the dreaming soul did not connote the union of the dreamer with the divine, as it did in the Middle Ages. Instead, it signified the soul's capacity for self-regulation and symbolization. Giordano Bruno (1548-1600), one of the precursors of modern science, was burned at the stake for refusing to recant his challenge to the biblical account of creation. Bruno, who espoused a naturalistic view of cosmology and of the origin of man, referred to the fact

that when the soul is at rest in relation to the outer senses, as in dreams, the images of perceptible things assume such clarity that when it dreams it does not think it is dreaming at all, for it is informed more accurately by a certain inner light than by an external one.

Bruno was calling attention to the hyperreal and hypervivid aspect of dreams that neuroscience has shown to be the result of increased activation of the visual brain. Leonardo da Vinci made the same point when he asked the question: "Why does the eye see things more clearly in dreams than the imagination, being awake?"

A late 15th-century French illumination of Petrarch asleep in the garden of his studio near Avignon corroborates what Bruno and Leonardo had in mind with respect to the origin and nature of dream visualization. The dreaming poet does not see, like medieval dreamers, an angel bearing a divinely sent, prophetic message. Instead, he has a vision of a meticulously rendered, realistic image of his allegorical poem, *The triumph of Love*, the inspiration for which, he tells us, came to him in a dream in which he saw Cupid, the Roman the god of love,

like one whom on the Campidoglio
a triumphal chariot conducts to great glory.

The illumination is an illustration in a French edition of Petrarch's sonnets and *Triumphs*. In the poet's dream vision the naked, blindfolded god of love with his beautifully colored wings stands on fiery embers. A triumphal chariot drawn by four white horses conducts him toward Venus, the goddess of love, who awaits his homage on an altar in her temple.

Despite the Renaissance emphasis on the physical reality and the physiological and psychological investigation of dreaming, 15th- and 16th-century writers did not abandon Macrobius' distinction between true dreams, which are prophetic and divinely inspired, and false dreams, which are not. The Neo-Platonic philosopher Marsilio Ficino (1433-1499) designated the dream state a kind of mental emptiness (vacatio mentis)

in which the soul, having taken leave of the body, is open to divine inspiration, especially in those whose minds are purged and turned toward God. The true dream is therefore of divine inspiration that touches only those who have already transcended the body in the waking state. Dreams which fail to fulfill this condition cannot claim to be true and to have a divine origin. Instead, they are derived from the influence of the senses, of the imagination (fantasia), and of plain thought. True dreams, however, require interpretation.

A generation later Agrippa of Nettesheim in his *De occulta philosophia* (1531-32) took a more ecumenical position. Like Ficino, he adhered to Macrobius's distinction between true and false dreams; and he attributed the prophetic dream to a pure and tranquil mind that receives the prophetic message either through illumination by the intellect, or by divine revelation; the most reliable prophetic dream consists of what the dreamer was thinking about when he went to sleep; if, for example, he is oppressed by cares of the flesh or is fasting, his dreams have no prophetic value.

THE THREAT TO MORALITY AND CONTROL

Two related themes can be detected beneath the surface of Renaissance efforts to come to terms with and account for the reality of dreaming. One is moral: how to deal with the impure material that is so often conjured up in dreams, The other is practical: how to tip the balance toward a greater proportion not only of acceptable but of transcendent dream content. These themes resonate in our day in persons who even in the wake of Freud are still made uncomfortable by the clear testimony of dreams of their own and others' carnal natures, and who insist that dreaming can be manipulated as a vehicle to sublimated self-realization. In a commentary on the cabalistic writings of Pico della Mirandola dreams are characterized as psychological states favorable to "imagined visions" that convey moral lessons in the guise of allegories.

The model for this idea was the warning to the dreamer in Macrobius' Commentary on Cicero's *Dream of Scipio* to resist the temptations of the life of pleasure (*voluptas*), and to pursue the path of virtue (*virtus*). The Dream of Scipio was the inspiration for one of the most engaging pictures, now in the National Gallery in London, by the young Raphael. It represents a somnium, a dream that is "true" but requires interpretation. The fact that the hero is dreaming is guaranteed by the presence in the center of the composition of a laurel tree. According to the 16th-century emblem book of Andrea Alciati, laurel possesses the property of foretelling the future and of making dreams come true. The knight's dream assumes the form of two women. One offers him a book and a sword, symbolizing the arduous path of virtus, suggested in the background by the steep rock and the spire rising above it. Her companion, symbolizing voluptas, offers the dreamer a flower. Raphael was here following a conception of morality advocated by Marsilio Ficino, who wrote in a letter to Lorenzo de' Medici that "there are three kinds of life: the contemplative, the active, and the pleasurable." The pursuit of any one of them at the expense

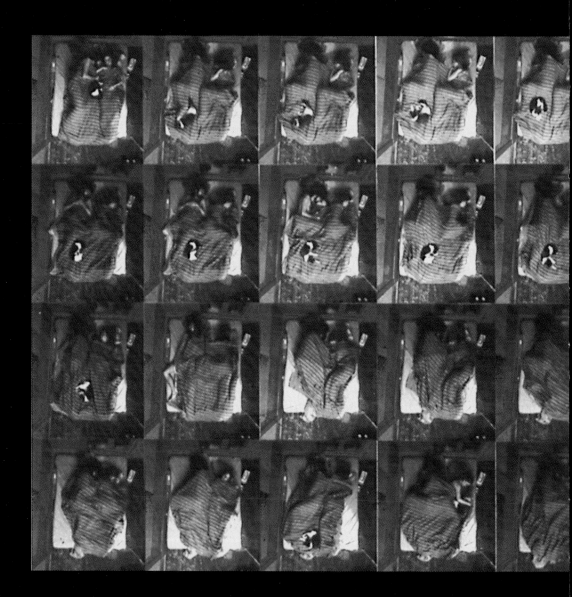

Josh and Judy were photographed by Theodore Spagna while sleeping at home with their cat.

Couples sleeping together synchronize their NREM-REM cycles because the posture shift of one bed partner causes a posture shift of the other. This is especially true in small beds, like the one that Josh and Judy shared.

Notice that the longest periods of immobility are seen early in the night when deep NREM sleep epochs occur. Later in the night, as sleep lightens, posture shifts become more frequent and finally become so disturbing to the cat that it leaves the bed. Then Judy gets up leaving Josh in bed alone.

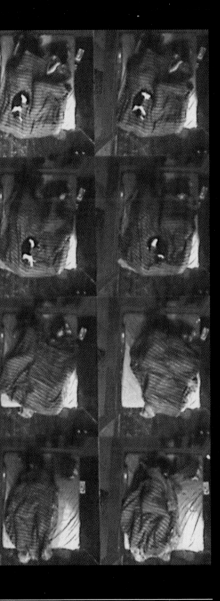

of the other two is wrong and contrary to nature. While the posture of Raphael's hero suggests that he is leaning toward the contemplative and active life of virtue, the gifts that the dream is bestowing on him also include the life of pleasure.

APPARITIONS AND NIGHTMARES

True dreams - the allegorical dream and the divinely sent vision - seem to have been less interesting to Renaissance artists than dreams that, according to Macrobius and later writers, have their origin in the physical and mental imbalance, distress, or confusion of the dreamer, and were therefore designated as false; and the ever greater command by artists in the representation of the human body and of human emotion provided them with the pictorial and technical means for the realistic depiction of false dreams, i.e. the phantasma, or apparition, and the insomnium, or nightmare. Botticelli's *Mars and Venus* in the National Gallery in London, as the art historian Charles Dempsey has shown, is a case in point.

The sleeping Mars is assailed by three playful satyrs, followers of the god Pan, who act as agents of a phantasma of sexual obsession in the sleeper's mind, the object of which is Venus. In classical mythology satyrs were demons who provoked sexual terror in the dreams of sleepers distressed by sensual error and confusion. The satyrs assailing Mars make lewd gestures toward Venus with their tongues, and have picked up Mars' jousting lance in order to poke a wasps' nest in the hollow of a tree against which his head rests and around which angry bees are beginning to swarm. The satyr, or paniscus, who blows in Mars' ear through a conch shell is an allusion to the myth that when Pan fought on the side of Zeus against the Titans he armed his companions with conch shells he found by the sea. When they blew through them the sound filled the

Titans with terror - known from that time on as panic - and put them to flight.

From a neurological point of view the phantasma is the evocation of hypnagogic hallucinations, especially of anxiety, caused by the activation of the limbic brain in REM sleep. Etymologically it corresponds to the Greek *panikos phobos*, sudden terror or panic that afflicts troubled minds. The theme of Botticelli's painting is a nightmare of sexual domination of a soul obsessed by the demons of its own moral confusion and preoccupation with erotic fantasies. The god of war, asleep in the shade of a tree, has removed his armor and dreams of Venus and love. But his dream is not a true vision of love. It is a dream of sensual desire and sexual possession, which in turn possesses him, an empty fantasy of Venus who is only a figment of Mars' own imagining that torments his slumbering spirit.

Although by Macrobius' lights the phantasma is internally generated and has no prophetic value, Botticelli nevertheless is also playfully reverting to the theory of an external agency in accounting for dream eroticism and dream anxiety. Both are in fact entirely natural and entirely normal: erotic dreams are universal, though rare. Sexual dream content has been acknowledged in less than three percent of dream reports of sexually active young adults, even when it was specifically asked for. Anxiety dreams, on the other hand, are extremely common. Roughly forty per cent of the dream reports following spontaneous awakening contain anxiety, often intensely unpleasant - such as the blast of the conch shell in the ear of Mars - but more often low-grade worry about being lost, unprepared, or unwelcome.

Sexual domination in the form of what in the Middle Ages would have been called a "rêve moralisée," a moralizing dream intended to teach a lesson, is also the theme of an engraving by Albrecht Dürer known as *The Dream of the Doctor*. A scholar who has fallen asleep has a vision of a classical Venus who turns toward him with an inviting gesture. At her feet a winged cupid is readying his bow. Sleep in the Middle Ages was identified with the vice of sloth, which begets lewdness because in their drowsiness sleepers are unable to resist temptation. In the upper part of the composition a grinning, bat-like demon tries literally to inflame the sleeper's carnal desires by blowing in his ear through a bellows. It is he who summons up the vision of Venus, whose realistically rendered nude body is as much the subject of the engraving as her role of erotic temptress with the power of *fascinatio* - of arousing sexual fantasies.

The most bizarre and enigmatic Renaissance picture of a false dream is a print of an unidentified subject by the early 16th-century engraver Marcantonio Raimondi. The engraving is known, as far as we know for no discernable reason, as *The Dream of Raphael*. The subject has also been identified as the dream of Hekuba, who before giving birth to Paris dreamt that she brought forth a firebrand that consumed the city of Troy, which the soothsayers interpreted as a prophecy that Paris would bring about the ruin of his country. The doubling of the figure of the sleeper has been thought to represent Hekuba seeing herself in her dream. Be that as it may, two uneasily sleeping female figures are surrounded by alarming, violent dream images: four small monsters at their feet, a burning building rising from a river or from flooded terrain, and a volcano erupting under dark clouds. Although these specific images are topical, the grim scenario is more or less congruent with the scientific account of dream emotion.

IMAGES OF THE INTERNAL SENSES

Renaissance scholars referred to dream images as "images of the internal senses." Toward the end of the fifteenth century the Florentine humanist Filippo Buonaccorsi,

Botticelli, Mars and
Venus, ca. 1480, National
Gallery, London.

The sleeping god of war
Mars is obsessed by a
nightmare, a form of
hypnagogic hallucination

that the Renaissance
called a *phantasma*, of
erotic fantasies and of
sexual domination

aroused by the goddess
of love Venus.

known as Callimaco Esperiente, rejected the view of Aristotle and other classical writers that dreams are formed from the remains of thoughts left over from waking. Instead, he conceived of dreaming and waking as complementary aspects of life: while we are alive we cannot cease to act, and nature has seen to it that in dreams we act no less than during waking; dreams are the dreamer's image of the world in accordance with his nature; their origin is not in external impulses, but in the mind and body of the dreamer. By the middle of the following century the Venetian scholar Gerolamo Fracostoro all but came within sight of the hypotheses of modern dream science. Building on the work of Callimaco Esperiente, Fracostoro concluded that dream images are produced by the ceaseless reworking in the mind during sleep of images gathered during waking in the form of *species*, the Latin term for what is visible, by which he meant images

of objects in the imagination that mediate between the mind and the world. They are equally active whether we are sleeping or awake; but because during sleep they are not coordinated by reason they are confusing, deceptive, and enigmatic.

In neurobiological terms the contrast in Marcantonio Raimondi's engraving between the women - or the woman seeing herself in her sleeping dream - wrapped in sleep and the frightening dream images denoting inner turmoil is due to the blockage during sleep of both external sensation and motor commands, as well as to primary activation of brain centers mediating emotion. This blockage shuts the brain off from the world around us, disassociating what is within from what is without. The mechanism by which dream images - "images of the internal senses" - are formed is now known to be the triggering of the sensory centers of the upper brain by stimuli arising

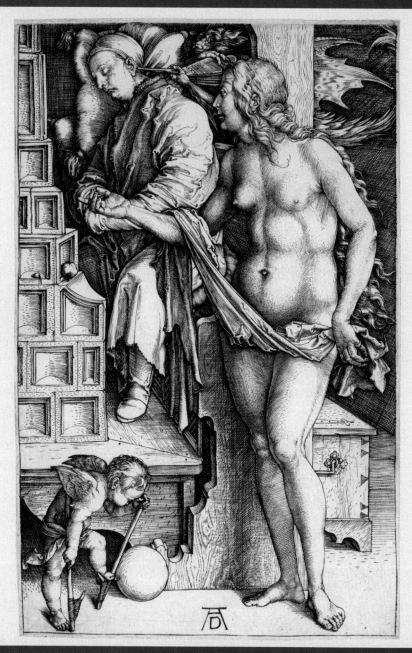

Albrecht Dürer, *The Dream of the Doctor*, *1497-1498, Albertina, Vienna*.

Like Botticelli's *Mars and Venus*, the subject of the engraving is a hallucination of sexual obsession. A sleeping scholar dreams that the goddess of love Venus turns to him with an inviting gesture. A winged demon, who has summoned Venus in her role as erotic temptress with the power of arousing sexual fantasies, inflames the scholar's carnal desire by blowing in his ear through a bellows.

from the lower brain. Internal images in dreams are not coordinated by reason because the frontal lobes of the brain are deactivated in REM sleep and cannot provide their usual organizational function. Fracostoro's intuition that dreams rework the input processed by the brain during waking has been confirmed by modern dream science in studies of the positive effects of sleep, especially of REM sleep, on learning. These studies suggest that sleep not only helps dreamers retain new material, but that in dreaming we generate images in order to facilitate visual discrimination in waking. This may be why images assume greater clarity, as Giordano Bruno and Leonardo perceived, than they do when we are awake.

MONSTERS AND DEMONIC DREAM IMAGERY

The four monsters at the feet of the dreaming women in the engraving by Marcantonio are members of the same family of metamorphic images as the demonic creatures in the *Temptation of St. Anthony* (1505-1506) in the Museu de Arte Antiga in Lisbon by Hieronymus Bosch who, according to Giovanni Paolo Lomazzo's *Treatise on the Art of Painting* (1584), "in the representation of apparitions and extraordinary and horrible dreams was unique and truly divine." Marcantonio's and Bosch's metamorphic inventions also belong to the same repertory of images as grotesques, a type of classical ornament revived in the Renaissance in which human, animal, and vegetal forms are combined in hybrid inventions which ancient and Renaissance writers interpreted as dream images and apparitions of a mind whose reason is in abeyance.

The Venetian humanist Daniele Barbaro (1513-1570) characterized grotesques as "deformities of nature, mixed of various species. Certainly as fantasies in a dream, they represent confusedly the images of things;" and he concluded that "without doubt we can call them the dreams of painting." The bizarreness and incongruity of grotesques prompted the Roman poet Horace (1st century BC) to compare their imagery - "a human head joined to the neck of a horse, feathers of many a hue spread over limbs picked up now here now there, so that what at the top is a lovely woman ends up below in a black and ugly fish" - to "a book whose idle fancies are shaped like a sick man's dreams, so that neither head nor foot can be assigned to a single shape." The works of Hieronymus Bosch were thought to have been inspired by dreams as early as 1521, when the Venetian chronicler Marcantonio Michiel described a painting by Bosch of *Hell*, with a forlorn seated figure surrounded by demons in the foreground as "representing a dream."

Bosch's consummate dream picture is the triptych known as *The Garden of Earthly Delights* in the Prado. It shows the creation of man in Paradise at the left; his folly and outlandish, bizarre sexual fantasies in the large central panel; and a ghoulish, terrifying vision of Hell - the drawing of the *Tree Man* that we discussed in chapter 1 is a study for its central image - on the right. By virtue of its wealth and inventiveness of detail and its technical virtuosity, the work has an unrivalled capacity for inducing in the viewer a delusional involvement in its hallucinatory imagery, whether frightening, as in the Hell panel, or sensual and erotic in the panel in the center.

If we could look as fixedly and closely at our dream images as we can at the three panels of *The Garden of Earthly Delights*, we might be as captivated by the artistic ingenuity of our dreams as we are by Bosch's painting. The problem of looking at dreams is that, unlike paintings, they don't sit still. Dreams are not only full of arresting detail, but the scenario in the dreaming mind's eye is constantly chang-

Raphael, *Dream of a Knight*, ca. 1505, National Gallery, London.

According to the Renaissance humanist Pico della Mirandola, dreams are favorable to "imagined visions" that convey moral lessons in the guise of allegories. The dreaming knight has a vision that presents him with the moral choice in the form of two female figures, one offering him a sword and a book, symbolizing the path of virtue, the other a flower, signifying the life of pleasure.

ing. When looking at a painting or a detail in a painting by Bosch, the closest we can get to the visuo-motor envelopment of dreaming is to run our eyes up, down, and across the composition. Dream scanning, by contrast, is involuntary. The dream images that fill our vision are replaced, in an instant, by other phantasmagoria as compelling as those before. And we can't look away, as we can from a painting.

Condensation as Image Fusion

In this connection there are two important points we would like to emphasize. One is the formal dream property of condensation, a fusion of aspects of two or more discrete objects into a single image. We consider this to be a special case of dream bizarreness, and as such a joint function of hyperassociativity, discontinuity, and incongruity. The central panel of *The Garden of Earthly Delights* illustrates our point. By condensation we do not mean the defensive transformation that Freud implied in using that term to describe one of the characteristics of what he called the dream work. For us Bosch's inventively and playfully erotic couples are what they appear to be: human beings driven by boundless sexual, animal instincts.

Our second point is that Bosch's emphasis, particularly in the images of the right-hand panel (on page 12), on the fusion of apparent opposites corresponds to the autocreative character of the dreaming brain. One need look no further than one's own dreams for evidence of the brain-mind's capacity to combine the most apparently incongruous elements into seamlessly integrated images, and to do so with hyperintense visual clarity and emotional resonance.

In contrast to the images of dreams in Renaissance art that we have discussed so far, a watercolor of a *Dream Vision* by Albrecht Dürer is unencumbered by mythological, moralizing, or other symbolic baggage that requires interpretation. It is an image of a dream as the dreamer dreamt it. In 1525 Dürer had a vision in his sleep that he described and illustrated in his journal:

On the night between Wednesday and Thursday after Pentecost (June 7-8, 1525) I saw in a dream what this sketch represents: a multitude of waters falling from the sky. The first struck the earth at a distance of four miles away; the shock and the noise were terrifying, and the whole land was inundated. I was so terrified that I awoke. Then the other columns of water, frightening in their violence and number, struck the earth, some further away, some nearer. And they fell from so high that they seemed to descend slowly. But when the first column had almost reached the earth, its fall became so swift and was accompanied by such wind and roaring, that I awoke, my whole body trembling, and it took a very long time for me to recover myself. So when I arose, I painted what is seen above. God turns all things to the best.

It has been thought that Dürer's dream is connected with a prediction published in 1499 that in 1524 a catastrophe of apocalyptic proportions would be caused by a conjunction of planets in the sign of Pisces. One-hundred-and-thirty-three editions of pamphlets by fifty-six scholars and astrologers were published between 1517 and 1524 confirming or condemning the prediction. Dürer's description of his dream includes but a slight variation on the passage in one of these pamphlets that "tremendous waters will fall with impetuous winds and thunderstorms;" and he repeated the pamphlet's concluding sentence: "God turns all things to the best."

Marguerite Yourcenar in an essay on Dürer's watercolor has made the point that the artist's account of his dream vision is unprecedented and unique in its detachment and objectivity. It does not evoke the drama of mankind's terror and despair in the face of the biblical deluge. Dürer observes the hallucinatory, cosmic vision realistically and with clinical precision, as if it were taking place in measurable, three-dimensional space. He gauges the distance of the waters' first impact and of the others in relation to it. He is aware of the apparent slowness and then the swiftness of the columns of falling water. There are no humanistic and theological allusions to man's insignificance confronted by the forces

Marcantonio Raimondi, *The Dream of Raphael*, ca. 1510, Harvard University Art Museums, Cambridge.

In neurobiological terms, the dream images denoting inner turmoil of the sleeping women - four small metamorphic monsters belonging to the same family of images as grotesques, a burning building, and an erupting volcano - arise from the activation during sleep of the brain centers mediating emotion, and the blockage that shuts the brain off from the outer world and allows it to spawn fearful fantasies.

of the universe. No vengeful angels announce the wrath of God.

THE PARADIGM SHIFT FROM PROPHECY TO ANTICIPATION

Dürer's realistic account and depiction of his dream coincided with a shift in explanations of the origin and nature of dreams by Renaissance scholars. In 1521 the Spanish humanist Juan Luis Vives published a critique of Macrobius' Commentary on the *Dream of Scipio* that brought to a conclusion the long tenure of Macrobius as the supreme authority on dreams and dreaming. In *Concerning Life and the Soul* (1538) Vives maintained that dreams, rather than being the "cause" of future events, are but "signals" of our mental and physical condition. He held that some of our nocturnal visions may fortuitously prove to be true if they are symbolically linked to a preceding passion or obsessive thought; that dreams can be put in our minds by God, as in the case of Pharaoh or Jacob; but that in most cases dreams are natural events to which we, misled "by passion or by a bold belief," assign a supernatural origin.

Vives agreed with Aristotle that dreams are residuary movements of our conscious life - that we "often dream of what we did or said the same day" because the same images are impressed on our fantasy through a "vehement disturbance of the soul" such as fear, anger, envy, or love; but that dreaming differs from waking inasmuch as in the dream state fantasy, "freed from the censorship of reason," draws material from memory "without any order or control." Whether this hyperassociative talent makes dreaming more or less cognitively useful than waking depends upon its context. It might be more useful creatively, and less useful analytically.

Like Gregory of Nyssa, who argued fifteen hundred years before Freud that dreams are motivated by passions which in the waking state are held in check by the intellect, Vives had an insight far ahead of his time. He believed that in dreams we "probe, investigate, reason, and find solutions to problems we could not resolve while awake." He was thus the first thinker to broach the much discussed subject of problem-solving in dreams. Vives' formulation of the idea that mental life is continuous in sleep and that when we dream we go on thinking also preceded by two-hundred years the similar observation in Diderot's *Encyclopédie* (1770) that

as soon as sleep has taken possession of our mental operations, the mind is subject to an uninterrupted series of representations and perceptions; but sometimes they are so confused or so dimly registered, that they do not leave the slightest trace, and this is in fact what we call 'deep sleep;' but we should be wrong to regard it as a total absence of any sort of perception, as complete mental inertia.

VOLITION VS. AUTOMATICITY

The same point was made soon thereafter, though with greater precision, by the French philosopher Maine de Biran (1766-1824). Maine de Biran defined sleep as a passive state characterized by the abeyance of the will and the absence of reflective awareness, as a result of which the mental processes in dreams are "automatic." These processes can assume two forms: "intuitive dreams or visions" in which the sleeper sees images and "phantoms of all colors and shapes," and dreams in which

the most extraordinary inventions [and] solutions to the most difficult problems may come to the mind of the sleeper, but always with that spontaneous insight which precludes or anticipates investigation and is compatible with the absence of will.

It was another two-hundred years before neuroscience discovered scientific evidence proving that Vives was right in his basic assumption that sleep mentation is active, continuous with waking, and creatively recombinatorial. The more specific claim that dreaming solves problems has been less easy to sustain. A few reported instances suggest that dreaming sometimes can provide very useful insights. For example, in 1920 the biochemist Otto Loewi was working on an experiment to show whether nerves send their messages chemically or electrically. The experiment that gave him the answer, that nerves transmit their signals chemically, came to him in a dream.

The most famous dreamer who found the answer to an unresolved problem in his sleep is René Descartes. Descartes denied that dreams are a source of knowledge, because knowledge comes only through the exercise of reason in the course of conscious thought. Yet a dream that he called his "dream of rationalism" changed the course of his life and thought.

Referring to himself in the third person, he tells us that for several years he struggled to

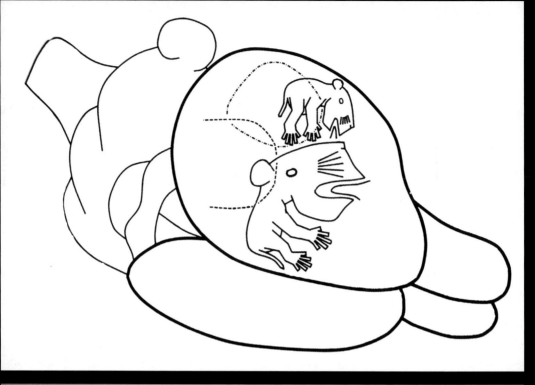

Sensory Ratunculus.

The surface of the body is represented on the surface of the brain where stimulation of the skin evokes electrical responses.

The drawings are bizarre because the size of the brain areas given over to mapping sensory stimuli differ greatly from the areas of skin represented. Thus the face and the

whiskers project to many more neurones than the trunk or the tail. The resulting chimera is also notable because it is reduplicated (SI and SII). Of course, there is no little

rat inside the rat's head but there is a map of the sensory surface of the body which can be activated by internal as well as external stimuli (Drawings by Clinton Woolsey).

clear his mind of prejudices and to make the pursuit of truth his life occupation. This endeavor

threw his mind into violent agitation that grew greater and greater, [and] so exhausted him that the fire went into his brain and he fell into a kind of enthusiasm which so mastered his already cast down mind that it prepared it to receive the impressions of dreams and visions.

During the night of the 10th of November, 1619, he had a dream "that he could only imagine had come to him from above." Descartes dreamt that he was given two books,

a dictionary and a book of poetry. While still dreaming, he interpreted the dictionary as standing for all the sciences, and the book of poetry as signifying philosophy and wisdom. When he awoke he understood that the dream was a command from Heaven that he should devote his life to the search for truth by applying the mathematical method to all other studies. We agree with Descartes' assertion that his dream came from above. Our sense, however, of the higher power responsible for the dream is different from his. It is our supposition that this rare example of on-line symbol interpretation came from the seat of reason in Descartes' frontal lobes, that he was in very light NREM sleep well into the night, and that his mind was already primed for the conclusion that he drew when he awoke.

In point of fact, dream thinking has been very sparsely studied. After sleep laboratory reports in the 1960s and 1970s showed that thinking was rare in REM sleep dreams, and only slightly more common in dreams during NREM sleep, the matter was dropped. Recently, however, Roar Fosse and Robert Stickgold, working on data collected from subjects sleeping at home whose mental activity was monitored at all hours of the day and night, have shown that that the paucity of thinking is the same regardless of whether subjects are dreaming at home or in the laboratory, and that in every successive cycle as well as during every night it occurs less frequently in REM than in non-REM sleep.

MATERIALISM AND THE ENLIGHTENMENT

By the time of Descartes, classical and medieval ideas of the nature and origin of dreams had been largely supplanted by the materialistic theories that became the ruling fashion of thought during the Enlightenment a century later, whether applied to dreams, the nature of man, or the conduct of human affairs. The gulf that separates medieval from 17th-century conceptions of dreaming could hardly be more clearly and sharply defined than by juxtaposing the depiction of the *Dream of Jacob* by the Spanish painter José de Ribera with the representation of the same subject in the 12th-century Lambeth Bible.

Ribera's Jacob is a weary traveler who has fallen asleep near a tree trunk by the side of the road with his head, as is written in Genesis, on a stone covered with a cloak. Behind him is a soft, luminous cloud bank; above him small, vaporous angels are ascending an invis-
ble ladder in a shaft of yellow light. The neb-

diousness and insubstantiality of the dream image emphasize the conception of the dream as the mental experience of the dreamer. Thus while the angelic paradigm of dream generation is still present, it has receded, and may now be read as a product of the imagination.

The connection between mental life and the brain was still not clear, however. Descartes could not convince himself that the brain and the mind are not separate entities and that they have no more in common than their origin in the mind of God. He made a differentiation between dreaming and waking on the ground that "our memory can never connect our dreams with one another as i

Do Cats Dream?

Of course we cannot have scientific proof that they do but we do not that they activate theirs brain in sleep just as we humans do and the mechanism of this brain activation appears to be the same as ours. In this drawing, the artist Sarah Landry imagines that if cats dream, they may dream of mice!

awake." But because we experience dreams as if they were happening in reality, he concluded that it is not possible to draw a clear distinction between dreaming and waking. In his *Meditations on Philosophy* (1641) he mused that

there is the fact that I am here, seated by the fire, attired in my dressing gown, having this paper in my hands. At the same time, how often has it happened to me that in the night I dreamt that I found myself in this particular place, that I was dressed and near the fire, whilst in reality I was undressed in bed...But in thinking over this I remind myself that on many occasions I have in sleep been deceived by similar illusions, and in dwelling carefully on this reflection I see so manifestly that there are no certain indications by which

we may clearly distinguish wakefulness from sleep that I am lost in astonishment, and my astonishment is such that it is almost capable of persuading me that I now dream.

Plato had found himself in the same quandary. "The question is asked," he wrote in the *Theaetetus*,

what proof you could give if anyone should ask us now, at the present moment, whether we are asleep and our thoughts are a dream, or whether we are awake and talking with one other in a waking condition.

For Descartes the difficulty stemmed from his conviction that waking and dreaming, insofar as they are true, are both, and in equal

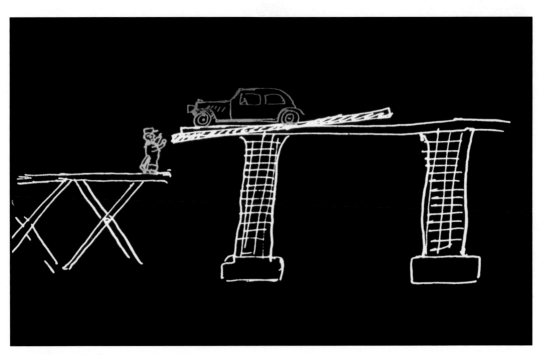

Dream Bridge.

The Engine Man was out in his car when the bridge suddenly changed level. This characteristic formal quality of dreams is called

discontinuity and is scored as such when we compare reports from different status of consciousness. Discontinuity, up to and including complete scene shifts, is a major

contributor to dream bizarreness. This drawing, by an amateur, should be compared to Paul Delvaux's discontinuous railway trestle in the middle of his painting on page 14.

In dreams times, places, persons, settings and actions may suddenly change without notice.

José de Ribera, The Dream of Jacob, 1639, Museo del Prado, Madrid.

In a depiction of the same subject as the illumination in the 12th-century Lambeth Bible (on page 60), small, vaporous figures of angels are ascending an invisible ladder in a shaft of yellow light. The nebulouness of the dream image illustrates the Renaissance approach to dreams as mental experiences generated in the sleeping mind of the dreamer rather than as brought to the dreamer by angels.

measure, subject to reason. "Whether we are awake or asleep," he wrote in the *Discourse on Method* (1637), "we should never allow ourselves to be persuaded except by the evidence of reason."

While we tend to agree with this assertion, we would add that self-observation and self-experimentation could have convinced both Plato and Descartes that dreaming and waking consciousness can be easily identified and distinguished, both after the fact and while experiencing one state or the other. The key to this discriminatory ability is the loss of cognitive power during dreaming, resulting in diminished self-awareness, orientational instability, and memory loss. In order to overcome the effects of these deprivations of our analytic powers during dreaming, we must enhance self-reflection by means of pre-sleep auto-suggestion. This allows reason back into the picture, as in the case of the conclusions Descartes drew from his dream of the two books.

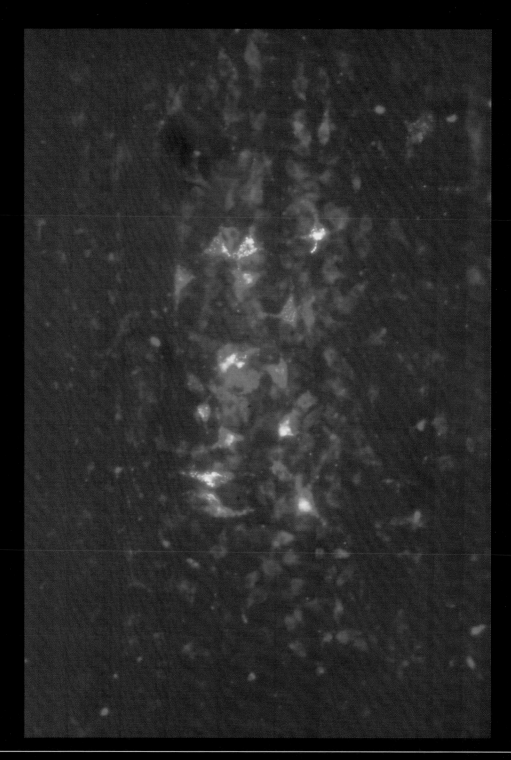

Serotonin Neurones.

In this photomicrograph by James Quatrocchi Raphe Nucleus Neurones glow fluorescently after a chemical which enhances REM sleep has been injected into the pontine reticular formation. Raphé nucleus neurones fire most frequently in waking and must be inhibited for dreaming to occur.

DREAMING AND THE UNCONSCIOUS MIND

There is no evidence in any of Descartes' writings that he had a clear conception of the unconscious mind. "The soul's nature or essence," he believed, "consists of its being conscious, just as the essence of the body consists in its being extended." It took half a century before the existence of unconscious thought - the notion that something goes on in the mind that we know nothing about - was acknowledged in *New Essays Concerning Human Understanding* (1704) by the mathematician, natural scientist, and philosopher Gottfried Wilhelm Leibnitz. "It is a great source of error," Leibnitz stated, "to believe that there is no perception in the mind but that of which it is conscious." Leibnitz based his argument that mental activity is continuous, even in sleep (against the claim of John Locke that it was temporarily suspended) on his concept of subliminal, or, as he called them, *petites perceptions*. We now know that brain activity is continuous across all mental states, including anesthesia. This obviates what have become fruitless arguments whether mental activity, be it conscious or unconscious, is continuous or not.

Fifty years after Leibnitz, G. C. Lichtenberg (1742-1799), finding in his own dreams ideas and images of which he was unaware while awake, first linked unconscious mental activity and dreaming; and as the 18th century drew to a close the unconscious came to be regarded as a source of the creative imagination. The idea of Friedrich von Schiller (1759-1805) that "poetry sets out from the unconscious" became one of the cornerstones of the Romantic movement. What Schiller and other thinkers were beginning to realize was that consciousness reflected but a small portion of brain activity, and that information processing, including the creative recombination of data, goes on without stopping under the surface of both waking and sleep. The nature of dreaming made this conclusion inescapably obvious.

Voltaire and the philosophes of the Enlightenment considered dreams as either irrational and verging on madness; or else, citing the authority of Hippocrates, as indices of bodily ailments. Hippocrates had suggested that to dream of springs or rivers raises the possibility of urogenital problems; and that dreaming of floods and inundations indicate the presence of too much blood and the need for the patient to be bled. In Diderot's *Encyclopédie* dreams are called

dispositions of the soul which survive in sleep and denote the state of body and soul; above all they have nothing in common with the occupations of the day; thus they are able to serve as diagnoses and prognostications in illnesses. These observations are all Hippocrates' and deserve exceptional attention by doctors; for it is undeniable that the dispositions of the soul influence and produce major changes in the body.

This neat example of Enlightenment rationalistic thought rests on easily identifiable erroneous premises. The "disposition of the soul" that survives in sleep and dreams is in fact a bodily state denoting brain activation; dreams may be disassociated from daytime experience, yet often reflect that experience, albeit in altered representations which, in turn, reflect the altered mode of brain activity in sleep. The extracerebral body has little or nothing to say in dreaming because the brain is cut off from it to the extent that most bodily sensations are dormant. Which is not to say that the mind doesn't influence the body. It does so because it is a function of the brain, and the brain is an integral part of the body.

THE SLEEP OF REASON

If we were to name an emblematic artistic document of the Enlightenment faith in reason we could hardly do better than Goya's etching

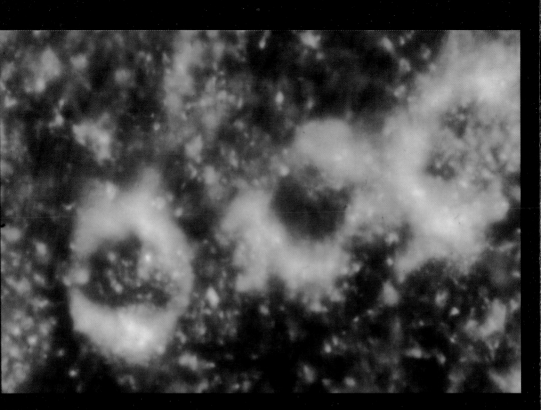

Norepinephrine Cells.

The brainstem contains neurones that manufacture and secrete chemicals called neuromodulators that determine the states of waking and dreaming. Cells of the nucleus locus coeruleus are made to fluoresce by staining the norepinephrine in them. These elements are called "Dream Cells" by the artist, Ragnhild Raingardt, who photographed the slides of Floyd Bloom for Dreamstage. Like the serotonin containing neurones seen on page 98, they cease firing in REM sleep.

El sueño de la razon produce monstruos. The composition was originally intended as the title page of a projected but never executed series of *Sueños* (Dreams). Instead, it became plate 43 of the *Caprichos*, a suite of etchings illustrating human folly and the dark forces in the soul from which spring superstition, witchcraft, and occult, satanic practices, to which the inscription under the preparatory drawing for the etching refers as "harmful common beliefs." While Goya's inscription is an expression of the Cartesian and Enlightenment belief that reason will prevail over the monsters of irrationality, it also points to a fundamental flaw in Descartes's thought. Descartes denied that dreams are true because he regarded truth and knowledge as identical, and knowledge as acquired through the application of the intellect. Yet except in the light of Descartes' mathematical model, truth is rarely, if ever, synonymous with rational knowledge. For Goya dreams spawned by "harmful common beliefs" in the abeyance of reason are true because that is how we experience them. The *Caprichos* are the "sound testimony" of this truth. Goya's etchings are the first direct, realistic depictions in the history of art of the description by Macrobius, more than a millennium before Goya, of the *phantasma* (apparition), in which the dreamer

seems to see crowding in on him strange moving or swimming forms, distorted in appearance and out of all natural proportion in size, or he may experience the rushing in of tumultuous whirling, kaleidoscopically changing things, either delightful or disturbing.

Goya's *Caprichos* coincided with a spate of writings on sleep and dreaming, subjects which interested scientists and philosophers for the light they could shed on the nature of consciousness. Their questions revolved around issues such as what becomes of consciousness during sleep; how and from where do ideas enter our minds; and whether any part of knowledge is of different origin from the rest. None of their writings, however, match the insight and power of Goya's images in the *Caprichos*. More than any other epoch, the 18th century insisted that all dreams have specific, identifiable, bodily or mental - physical or cerebral - causes. Among writers on dreams of Goya's time, one who came closest to the spirit of the *Caprichos* was Gottfried Heinrich Schubert. In *The Symbolism of Dreams* (1814) Schubert contrasted the visual language of dreaming, which he called hieroglyphic, with the verbal language of waking life; and he anticipated Freud's *Interpretation of Dreams* with the observation that dreams often have an amoral and demonic character because suppressed aspects of the personality come to the fore during sleep.

Ludwig Heinrich von Jakob in an essay published in 1791 effectively supplanted the materialistic psychology of dreaming of the Enlightenment with the theory that dreams are produced by a combination of the exclusion from consciousness of the "exterior senses" and the intense, playful activity during sleep of the "internal senses" and the imagination:

The dream is the state in which the nervous system is sufficient to activate the imagination but not the senses. The intellect has no power over volition, and the imagination alone is conscious

of representations. The intellect associates these with certain precepts, but its action is weak. It also confuses images with real objects. The poetic faculty plays with these activated representations, combines them, and creates new images. Dreaming is nothing but involuntary poetry.

The association of dreaming and poetry was to be one of the recurrent themes of Romanticism.

DREAMING: A THIRD STATE OF EXISTENCE

In his *Essay on the Intellectual Powers of Man* (1785) Thomas Reid, who from the age of fourteen suffered for almost two years from repeated nightmares, introduced the idea that dreams occur in an "intermediate" or "third state of existence" between sleeping and waking, a phrase used first by Frederick Snyder and by other scientists today to characterize REM, or dreaming sleep. Snyder and the French physiologist Michel Jouvet were also the first to advance functional theories of sleep that fit the general model of evolution proposed by Charles Darwin. According to Snyder, REM sleep evolved to permit animals to avoid predation by punctuating their sleep with arousals. Jouvet believed that because REM sleep is controlled by the brainstem, and because the brainstem is a phylogenetically primitive tool, REM sleep would be found in sub-mammalian species. Both Snyder's and Jouvet's hypotheses turned out to be wrong, an instructive example of how quickly science can correct itself and opens the doors to new ideas.

Erasmus Darwin, the grandfather of Charles Darwin and the author of *The Botanic Garden* (1791), regarded dreams as delusions and deceptions, for while we dream "we are so much absorbed in the contemplation of what passes in our imagination, that we

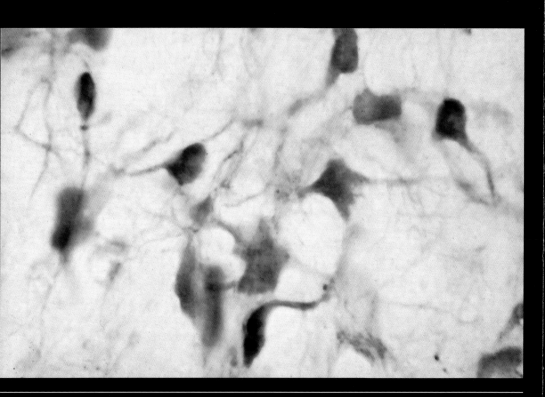

Acetylcholine Containing Cells.

Neurones which manufacture and secrete acetylcholine can be visualized by staining the enzyme choline acetyltransferase as in this slide provided by Marcel Mesulam. Since acetylcholine is secreted in REM sleep, it has been proposed that it may mediate and modulate that state. This hypothesis has been confirmed by the microinjection of acetylcholine enhancing or imitating drugs into the reticular formation and producing massive increases in REM sleep. An inference is that brain activation by acetylcholine, in the absence of norepinephrine and serotonin produced dream consciousness while brain activation by acetylcholine in the presence of norepinephrine and serotonin produces waking consciousness. We can thus begin to speak of a specific neurochemistry of conscious experience and differentiate different kinds of consciousness in terms of brain chemistry. No wonder artists and other visionaries have been so fascinated by dreaming. The popularity of mind-altering drugs is also more understandable given the brain's own chemical capacity to alter its state.

believe things present before our eyes, which are not so." He surmised, and modern dream science has corroborated, that dreams are experienced as delusions because "in sleep there is a total suspension of our voluntary power over ideas in our minds," and because we cannot compare ideas "passing in our imagination in sleep with our previous knowledge of things, and thus cannot perceive their incongruity."

The English philosopher David Hartley, like his contemporaries, considered the brain part of the body. In his *Observations on Man* (1801) he concluded that

> *dreams are nothing but the imagination, fancies, or reveries of a sleeping man; and they are deducible from the following three causes. First, the impressions and ideas lately received; and particularly those of the preceding day. Secondly, the state of the body, particularly the stomach and the brain; and thirdly, association.*

Hartley's terse formulation marks a true

paradigm shift in the history of dream theory. Having noticed, as had many of his predecessors, the distinctive phenomenology of dreaming, he formulated a tripartite causal hypothesis: (1) Dreaming, however bizarre, reflects recent cognitive experience; (2) dreaming is dependent on the state of the brain; (3) dream cognition reflects altered associative processing.

But Hartley went well beyond these hypotheses. On the basis of his recognition that associative processes were altered - in fact loosened - in dreaming, he proposed that this enabled the brain to be cognitively flexible. Advancing his notion that dreaming is useful precisely because it loosened associations, Hartley went so far as to suggest that a natural tendency to obsess and perseverate was thereby reduced. If associations were only enhanced, and he assumed that some were, we would all become idiot savants, spouting out-dated time tables and telephone numbers. Hartley believed that the heightened representation in dreaming of recent experience signaled the brain's interest in novelty and that in this way the mind's knowledge bank was constantly updated. At the same time, older obsolete data could be discarded. This was the first specific cognitive theory of dreaming, and it is still being tested today.

By virtue of his emphasis on the brain processes underlying these plastic changes, Hartley was the father of British associativism, the dominant school of psychology in the 19th century, and a progenitor of modern cognitive neuroscience. As for his relevance to art and more specifically to the Romantic movement we need not speculate. Hartley exercised so powerful an influence on Samuel Coleridge that before the poet collaborated with Wordsworth in the composition of the *Lyrical Ballads* (1799), he struggled to forge a consilience between poetry and psychology on the basis of associativism. And he named his son Hartley.

John Anster Fitzgerald, *The Nightmare*, 1851-1852, *Private Collection, United Kingdom.*

The dreaming girl is writhing on her bed, surrounded by goblins who offer her red and yellow drinks that match the medicine bottles on her bedside table, suggesting that her dream is drug-induced. In the background her ghostly figure enacts three dream scenarios of gathering menace: she embraces a lover under a full moon, she is waylaid by two masked figures with swords, and she turns away from a kneeling man while another masked man and a masked woman flee.

Mind in the Balance

Rationalism vs. Romanticism

> *The painter should paint not only what he sees*
> *before him, but also what he sees within.*
> *But if he sees nothing within himself,*
> *he should also desist from painting*
> *what he sees before him.*

Caspar David Friedrich *(1774-1840)*

The materialistic vision of the Enlightenment prompted the appropriation of dreams and ecstatic states in the service of Romanticism. By submitting the physiology and psychology of dreams to systematic observation and study, scientists and philosophers anticipated the hypothesis of modern neuroscience that dreams are the product of activation mechanisms in the brain, whose cellular and molecular basis can be quantified and, to a degree, experimentally controlled.

Artists and poets too observed and kept records of their dreams. The notebooks of Coleridge are filled with comments on the bizarreness of his dreams, on their relationship to his waking life, and, like the descriptions by modern dream researchers of the activity of the brain in REM sleep, on the mechanics and levels of dreaming. In the history of all the arts after the turn of the 18th century an increased insistence on inspiration is detectable, to the point where dreams could be painted or put into words, a trend which in the representational arts leads from Goya to Surrealism. The Romantic poet Novalis (1772-1802) insisted that dreams are the same stuff as poetry, and that both conferred

higher meaning on the everyday, a mysterious
cast on the habitual, the aura of the unknown on
the known, the luster of infinity on the finite.

Sharpening vs. Blurring of Boundaries

The general proposition of the 18th century was that all things are reducible to an underlying, rational structure. The Romantics regarded this as profoundly false. The aim of Romanticism was to break down the barriers between dreams and waking, between the conscious and the unconscious, between illusion and reality. In a story by E.T.A. Hoffmann (1766-1822) about a city councilor, a brass knocker outside his door at times turns

Gérard Grandville, Crime and Punishment, 1847, Nancy, Bibliothèque Municipale.

Grandville's drawing illustrates the sequential transformation of images that is one of the formal characteristics of dreams. The cross at the top becomes the scales of justice, then a series of eyes, which evolve into a man-eating school of fish whose victim is, in turn, reaching for a cross.

into an apple vendor; and when Hoffmann was walking across a bridge in Berlin he often felt as if he were encapsulated in a glass bottle, and was not sure whether the people he saw around him were human beings or dolls. While this was no doubt a case of psychological delusion, a recurrent motif in Hoffmann's fiction is the transformation that we experience in dreams of everything turning into everything else. "The dream," Novalis wrote in one of his fragments, "informs us in a curious fashion about the soul's ability to penetrate and transform itself into every object."

The pluripotential plasticity by which perceptual cognition and emotional metamorphosis may be achieved is afforded, we now know, by the dramatic shift in brain neuromodulatory balance that distinguishes REM sleep from waking. But the capacity to associate more freely, more loosely, and more creatively can be enhanced by any movement along the continuum between alert waking and REM sleep. Movement along this continuum is in fact required to achieve the conditions of free associations sought be Freud, and by hypnotists before and since Freud who wished to induce the extreme plasticity of hypnotic trance.

Sequences of transformations characteristic of dreams were a favorite theme of the French illustrator Gérard Grandville. In his drawing *Crime and Punishment* the initial image of a cross at the top of the composition becomes the scales of justice, then a series of eyes becoming larger and smaller, which further evolve into a man-eating school of fish whose victim comes full circle by reaching for a cross. In a letter to Eduard Charton, the editor of *Magasin Pittoresque*, where the engraving of the drawing was published, Grandville referred to it as an example of "nocturnal visions and transformations," and explained that it should be read from the upper left to the lower right, "where the dream ends." The title, which is not

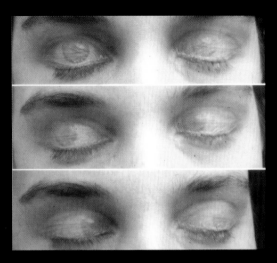

Moving Eyes.

How can we represent the eye movements of sleep in humans? While it is possible to film such movements in sleeping cats and to capture REM's in video studies of the human face, their depiction in still images is a challenge. To meet that challenge we took double exposure shots of an awake subject who moved his eyes from right to left with his lids open and closed. The resulting image has been reproduced in numerous textbooks of psychology because it captures, by a visual trick, the essence of REM sleep. The picture is called "moving eyes."

Grandville's but Charton's, clearly identifies the dream's two episodes: the crime in the upper left corner, and its expiation on the rest of the page.

While Freud would have interpreted these trains of associations as disguised symbols of the dreamer's unconscious wishes, modern dream science suggests that they directly and transparently reveal instinctual forces. Grandville himself was of the opinion that

we do not dream of any object that we have not seen or thought about while awake. It is the amalgam of diverse objects perceived in the mind at often considerable distances that form the strange and heterogeneous combination of images in our dreams.

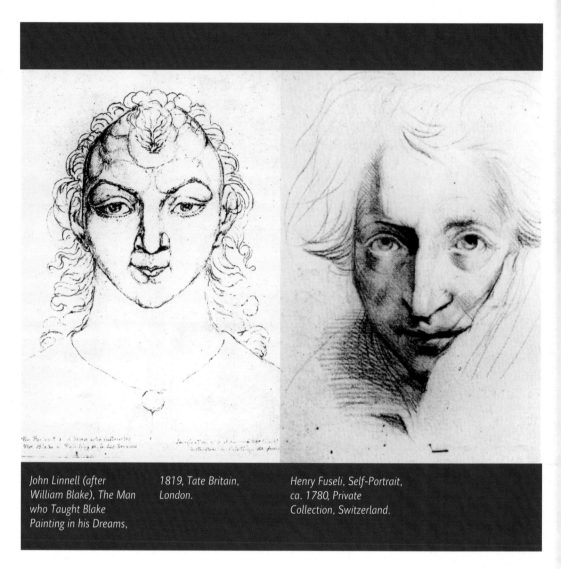

John Linnell (after William Blake), The Man who Taught Blake Painting in his Dreams, 1819, Tate Britain, London.

Henry Fuseli, Self-Portrait, ca. 1780, Private Collection, Switzerland.

It was difficult for many early exponents of dream plasticity to appreciate just how far it could be taken. To say that we don't dream of any object we have not seen when awake is to underestimate the transformative power of the brain. Grandville's rendering of dream image sequences are admirable for their emphasis upon the serial associations. On the other hand, his depiction of each successive image as if it were a photographic representation of waking visual reality does not do justice to the uniqueness and originality of dream images, such as the wondrous creation of the double bicycle, the desk-top computer, and the flying carpet in the journal of the Engine Man. None of these objects was ever seen, as such, in his waking, daily life.

THE CELEBRATION OF DISSOCIATION

The Romantics believed that creation in art and science stems not from logical reasoning, but emerges as a sudden insight in a state of consciousness in which, as in dreams, attention is defocused, thought is associative, and a large number of mental representations are simultaneously activated. Recent research has corroborated the association of the creative process in art with dreaming and with the internal mechanisms of the brain; and it has led the neurophysiologist, Semir Zeki, to conclude that

the function of the visual brain - a search for constancies with the aim of obtaining knowledge of the world - is applicable with equal vigor to the function of art...Artists are neurologists, studying the brain with techniques that are unique to them, exploiting the parallel-processing system of the brain to create their works, and reaching interesting but unspecified conclusions.

For the visionary poet and painter William Blake dreams were intimations of the immanence of God. Among his many depictions of dreams, many inspired by Milton and Shakespeare, the *Dream of Jacob*, a subject of Christian art from the 12th century onward, provided him with an opportunity for expressing in pictorial form his belief that dreams were the road to the experience of the divine. We know that for Blake, like for other Romantic artists, dream experiences, visions, and hallucinations were integral components of the creative process. Blake was a confirmed Swe-

denborgian. Just as the Swedish scientist-turned-mystic Emmanuel Swedenborg met God and his angels in his dreams and conceived of the Church of the New Jerusalem on the basis of their oneiric guidance, so Blake was to meet a man in his dreams from whom he received instruction in painting.

Below a tracing by Blake's friend John Linnell of one of the artist's drawings of Spirit Heads Linnel wrote: "The portrait of a Man who instructed Mr. Blake in Painting etc. in his Dreams." We do not know whether Blake consciously incubated his oneiric assistant. We do know, however, that such figures can be summoned by auto-suggestion. In 1867 the French scientist Hervey de Saint-Denis in *Les rêves et les moyens de les diriger* (Dreams And How To Direct Them) published evidence based on the observation of his own dreams that dreaming can be influenced by conscious intent during waking, and that waking consciousness can be partially achieved while dreaming. In this state of so-called "lucid dreaming" it is possible for the artist to tap primordial material and to give it form by combining it, in the words of Paul Klee, "with the proper pictorial elements."

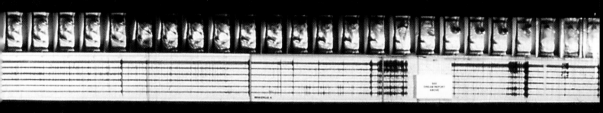

Allen Moore Sleeps, Dreams, and Awakens in the Sleep Lab.

In this long sequence from the end of the night, Allen Moore goes from NREM to REM to wake. After going to the bathroom, he records his dream.

Henry Fuseli, *The Nightmare, 1781, Detroit Institute of Arts.*

The nightmare vision takes the form of a horse who peers through a curtain with wild eyes, and an incubus squatting on the sleeper's belly. The apparition of the horse and the incubus in neurobiological terms is the product of the periodic internal activation of the brain and the cardiorespiratory system during sleep.

Prescribing Dreaming with Drugs

We know that Blake, Coleridge, Thomas de Quincey, and other nineteenth-century artist and poets induced and manipulated their dreams. In order to achieve dream-like, hallucinatory states they used opium, cocaine, heroin, or peyote cactus buds, which enhance or interfere with the brain chemicals norepinephrine and acetylcholine, and thus produce the modulatory changes that distinguish dreaming from waking. Coleridge and de Quincey also attributed to altered states of consciousness the creation of imagery in works of art that reminded them of their own visionary experiences. In *The Confessions of an English Opium Eater*, de Quincey remembered that Colerdige once described to him a set of plates by Piranesi - no doubt Piranesi's engravings of imaginary *Carceri* (prisons) - that "recorded the scenery of his visions during the delirium of a fever." Some represented "vast Gothic halls" with aerial flights of stairs which ultimately "are lost in the upper gloom of the hall. With the same power of endless growth and self-reproduction," de Quincey tells us, "did my architecture proceed in my dreams."

The Victorian fairy painter John Anster Fitzgerald (1823-1906) discovered his true vocation in a series of dream paintings in which sleepers are assailed by drug-induced hallucinations of hideous creatures from fairy land resembling the grotesque figures and metamorphic monsters of Hieronymus Bosch. In *The Artist's Dream* (on page 50) the painter has fallen asleep in front of his easel on which there is a painting of a fairy. In his dream he sees the model turn her head to look at him. The artist is Fitzgerald himself, the beautiful fairy is the heroine of the romantic ballet *Sylphide*, and the elves and goblins are members of the cast of dream-induced monsters that populate his dream paintings.

Fitzgerald's self-portrait of the artist as dreamer was followed by a trio of dreaming girls. In *The Nightmare* the girl writhes in anguish on her bed. The wreath that she wears in the background dream sequence has fallen on her pillow. Her ghostly figure is shown enacting three episodes of gathering menace among a band of revelers in 17th-century costume, some of whom are masked. She is shown under a full moon, embracing a lover; she is waylaid by two masked figures with swords; she turns away from a kneeling man, while a masked man and a masked woman flee. Lying on her bed, she has changed from the thin white costume of her ghostly apparition to a heavily embroidered Turkish jacket and brilliantly colored silk sash which falls onto the bed, with the fringe touching the floor, resembling a pool of blood running down from a wound. Around her bed goblins offer red and yellow drinks from a steaming bowl, matching the color of the fluid in two medicine bottles on her bedside table. The girl's sleep is clearly drugged.

In the two successive versions of the dreaming girl, entitled *The Stuff That Dreams Are Made Of*, the explicit references to narcotics are toned down; they are hallucinatory dreams of fairyland figures rather than horrible nightmares. In the first version Fitzgerald anticipated modern neuroscience by centering his subject's hallucinatory imagery in her sleeping head on which a battery of fairies fix their impish gaze. Today we can go further and look *inside* the sleeper's head. When we enter REM sleep and experience dream consciousness, the visions that appear arise from the activation and modulation of brainstem neurones that move the eyes and send signals to the visual centers of the upper brain. We no longer need fairies to explain the visions of dream consciousness.

Francisco Goya, *The Dream of Reason Produces Monsters*, 1797, Museo del Prado, Madrid.

Goya's title refers to the Enlightenment belief that reason will prevail over the monsters of irrationality that are generated by the dreaming brain while reason is asleep. The drawing is the first realistic depictions in the history of art of the description by the 5th-century writer Macrobius of the nightmare as a *phantasma*, in which the dreamer sees crowding and rushing in on him strangely moving, tumultuous, whirling forms.

Nightmares and the Art of the Incubus

Coleridge used opium in order to try to banish the nightmares that plagued him all of his life. "With sleep," he wrote, "my horrors commence." Yet nightmares also fascinated him. Like the Swiss-born painter Henry Fuseli, who thought that dreams are "one of the most unexplored regions of art," Coleridge believed that troubled sleep and dreams could put him in touch with his creative self. Fuseli made some forty variations on the subject of nightmares. He painted *The Nightmare* (1781) now in the Detroit Institute of Arts for an exhibition at the Royal Academy of Arts in London. When it was exhibited in 1782 the painting was considered unequalled in originality of conception. It was subsequently engraved, and proved so popular that the publisher made a profit of 500 pounds from the sale of the print. The painting was also the subject of a poem by the naturalist Erasmus Darwin, whose *The Botanic Garden* was illustrated by both Blake and Fuseli:

So on his Nightmare, through the evening fog,
Flirts the squat fiend o'er fen, lake, and bog:
Seeks some love-wilder'd maid with sleep oppress'd
Alights, and grinning sits upon her breast –
Such as of late, amid the murky sky,
Was marked by Fuseli's poetic eye;
Back o'er her pillow sinks her blushing head,
Her snow-white limbs hang helpless from the bed;
While with quick sighs and suffocating breath,
Her interrupted heart-pulse swims in death.

Fuseli's *Nightmare* shows not what the sleeper sees but what she feels. The nightmare vision takes the form of a horse who peers through a curtain with wild eyes - in the 19th century it was still believed in a part of Switzerland that nightmares assume the guise of a steed who stares at the sleeper with glowing eyes - and of an incubus who squats on the sleeper's belly. The incubus was a symbol of nightmares from late antiquity onward. According to Macrobius, the *phantasma*, or dream apparition, may take the form of an incubus, which "rushes upon people in their sleep and presses on them with a weight they can feel;" and Robert Burton wrote in *The Anatomy of Melancholy* (1621) that

sleepers, which by reason of humours and concourse of vapours troubling the phantasy, imagine many times absurd and prodigious things, and in such as are troubled with incubus, or witch ridden; if they lie on their backs, they suppose an old woman rides or sits so hard upon them that they are almost stifled for want of breath.

In neurobiological terms, the horse and the incubus are the products of the periodic internal activation of the brain and the cardiorespiratory system. In Fuseli's painting they are, of course, only symbols of these interal brain processes.

Sleep Medicine Before Its Time

Yet with his nightmare series Fuseli was in fact crossing the threshold of sleep pathology and presaging the development of modern sleep science. Such dramatic alterations in normal cardiorespiratory physiology as Fuseli's image symbolically represents must have been already in his time not only psychologically disturbing but medically disabling or even lethal.

Modern sleep science has abundantly demonstrated the natural tendency of breathing efforts to cease for dangerously long periods in sleep. This unwelcome but surprising-

William Blake, *The Dream of Jacob*, 1800-1803, *British Museum, London*.

Blake has interpreted Jacob's dream, also illustrated in the 12th-century Lambeth Bible (on page 60) and by Ribera (on page 97) in accordance with his belief, which he shared with other Romantic artists and writers, that dreams are the vehicle for the experience of the divine.

ly common trait is called sleep apnea. It is more common in men than in women, and represents an alteration in the discharge of the neurones which normally command breathing. When effective breathing is made more difficult by the muscular relaxation in sleep that causes snoring, the sleeper is in double trouble because compensatory breathing efforts may actually result in blockage of the airway. Fuseli's portly courtesans may thus have been prone to numerous nocturnal awakenings. The popularity of Fuseli's *Nightmare* image may have been subliminally recognized for its medical accuracy as well as its exotic overtones.

Fuseli had entered the Zwinglian ministry of the Swiss Protestant Church at the insistence of his artist father who thought that his son lacked the talent to be a painter. At age twenty he fled from Zurich to London. Steeped in the writings of Dante, Milton, and Shakespeare, and in the ideas of the German *Sturm und Drang* movement, he considered himself a writer. He had never painted. At twenty-seven he consulted Sir Joshua Reynolds, then president of the Royal Academy, about an artistic career. Reynolds prescribed a two-year sojourn in Rome at the feet of Michelangelo. Fuseli stayed in Rome for eight years (1771-1779), reading Goethe's *Sorrows of Young Werther* and imbibing the extroverted sensuousness of the Renaissance and the Baroque.

During those same years William Blake, who shared Fuseli's fascination with dreams, was copying medieval religious and visionary paintings and reading the Bible. Blake's mission was to portray divine inspiration; Fuseli's was to reconcile art and life, spirit and flesh.

On his way back to London in 1779 Fuseli stopped in Zurich, where he met and fell in love with Anna Landholt, the niece of his friend, the physiognomist Johann Kaspar Lavater. Anna's father opposed the liaison with the penniless artist, and Fuseli left for London without declaring his love. But what he could not achieve by day, he mastered by night. In a letter of June 16, 1779 to Lavater he described a dream of possessing Anna:

Last night I had her in bed with me, tossed my bedclothes hugger-mugger, wound my hot and tight-clasped hands around her, fused her body and her soul with my own, poured into her my spirit, breath and strength. Anyone who touches her now commits adultery and incest. She is mine and I am hers.

In the meantime Anna, whose portrait by Fuseli appears on the back of the canvas of *The Nightmare*, had married. The painting's obsessively erotic imagery, provoking fantasies of sexual violence and aggression as well as sensations of fear, suggests that the artist may have been venting his jealousy and rage on Anna by means of a malevolent dream.

If the genesis of such states is due to the nocturnal visitation of demons, how could the dreamer be held responsible for his oneiric experiences? If the nightmare and the erotic dream are both spontaneously generated by the sleeping brain, how could one explain the terror of the one and the delight of the other? And if, as Fuseli's *Nightmare* suggests, we are simply possessed in our dreams by phantoms arising from the depths of our brain-mind in sleep, how could we explain the fact that our oneiric visions can be both positive and negative - either "disturbing or delightful," as Macrobius put it - by a theory that is not mechanistic and psychologically ambivalent? To a degree that Blake would have considered heretical, Fuseli seems to have accepted the evidence that to be human is to be both good and evil, both fearful and vengeful, both pure and corrupt.

A nightmare of a different kind is the subject of one of eighteen canvases by Louis Janmot illustrating the *Poem of the Human*

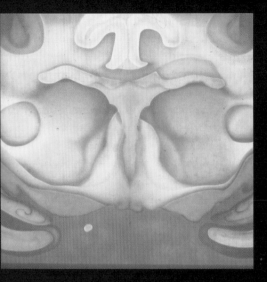

Soul, the story of the journey of the soul, personified by a man and woman at various stages of life from birth and childhood to old age, death, and transfiguration, which Janmot composed in 1835 in Rome while he was a student of Ingres at the French Academy. Janmot was a champion of the struggle during the July Monarchy and the Second Empire for the restoration of Catholicism.

Janmot's *Nightmare* is a protest against the secularization of knowledge and education introduced by the French Revolution, specifically against the transfer of control over school curricula from the church to the state. The boy and girl are pursued in a subterranean funerary gallery by a sorceress who holds the keys to the temple of false, secular knowledge. She has already seized the girl, who has fainted in her arms, and is about to capture the terrorized boy, who does not see the pavement disappearing in front of him. The pernicious nature of the learned professors is revealed in their grotesque faces which, in place of funerary urns, look out from windows behind arches.

The passage in the poem that the painting illustrates denounces the horrors incurred in the prison of the secularized university, symbolized by the funerary gallery, and the vio-

lence inflicted on children separated by the state from their families. The sorceress with wild eyes, a malignant inversion of the maternal figure from whom the children have been ripped, personifies baleful science, which in the absence of faith irrevocably leads to death. Quite apart from its political message, the painting is an undisguised evocation of the fear and terror we experience in bad dreams.

Janmot would have suffered even more dire nightmares if he could have imagined what the further secularization of the University of Lyon would do to the safe and secure world of Catholic faith in the succeeding century. By the time Michel Jouvet established his sleep research unit in Lyon in the late 1950s the nightmare of false knowledge that Janmot abhorred was coalescing with the normative science of the modern world. Among the many French scientists who worked there very few were of Janmot's persuasion. The "baleful science" of which Janmot complained was, on another reading, an escape from the oppression of cloistered learning, a liberation of the mind from scholastic doctrine, and a ticket out of provincial isolation onto a larger, international intellectual stage.

Strange Bedfellows and Their Monstrous Offspring

A fascination with the philosophical and moral implications of sleep and dreams was not the only passion shared by Blake and Fuseli. Both admired and drew inspiration from Milton nd Shakespeare. They applauded the ideals of the French Revolution; and they witnessed its inevitable failures. On the way to a falling out of their own - largely because Blake was incapable of executing Fuseli's engravings without embellishing them with ideas of his own - they formed a curious love triangle with the feminist Mary Wollstonecraft. Blake was so captivated by her that he proposed a ménage à trois with his wife Catherine. But Mary had set her sights on Fuseli, and proposed that he and his newly-wed wife Sophia visit Paris with her and the publisher Joseph Johnson. To Fuseli's great relief, Sophia refused. Undaunted, Mary Wollstonecraft went to Paris anyway. On her return to London Mary took up with the free-thinker William Godwin, only to die giving birth to her second child.

Under the name of Mary Shelley, this daughter was to become a more famous writer than her mother. At age seventeen she eloped with the poet Percy Bysshe Shelley. While she and Shelley were romantically exiled in Switzerland, she responded to Byron's request for a ghost story by writing *Frankenstein or the Modern Prometheus* (1818), a fusion of Fuseli's nightmare vision and Blake's dream mystique in a nocturnal monster more horrible than either could have imagined.

The root of the idea that a human being could be fabricated by galvanizing the body parts of corpses was derived from the evolutionary theories of Erasmus Darwin. "Invention," Mary Shelley wrote, "does not consist in creating out of the void, but out of chaos." Creation, like dreaming, is the aleatory activation of old parts resulting in a new synthesis, whether in the projection of the horse and demon in Fuseli's *Nightmare*, or the composition of Frankenstein's monster. Conceived at night and wreking its vengeance by moonlight, the bionic creature murders his creator's newly-wed wife on her nuptial bed before her love can be consummated. Mary Shelley's description of Elizabeth dead could well be a caption for Fuseli's painting:

She was there, lifeless and inanimate, thrown across the bed, her hair hanging down and her pale and distorted features half covered by her hair. Everywhere I turn I see the same figure, her bloodless arms and relaxed form flung by the murderer on its bridal bier.

Born during the period of Romanticism, the modern scientific vision of dreaming has recourse only to romances that are biological. Our night visions and nightmares are by turns disturbing and delightful because our brains are periodically activated by electro-chemical switches, and our minds are fooled into seeing and believing the impossible by sparks of our own unconscious, material devising. While the materialistic view of the mind of neuroscience reduces us to mechanical robots subject to determinism and automaticity, it also, as Mary Shelley surmised, implies the freedom and creativity that derives from chaos.

Dreaming and Madness

A combination of factors - the impact of Mary Shelley's Frankenstein, the taste for the evocation of terror in the Gothic novel, the fascination of the Romantics with troubled sleep, and the popularity of Fuseli's *Nightmare* - launched a fashion for the depiction of hallucinatory nightmare vision throughout the nineteenth century. In 1795 the Swedish sculptor Johan Tobias Sergel made a rapid, feverishly

Odilon Redon, Vision, 1879, Chicago Art Institute.

The vision in a lithograph from the album *Dans le rêve* was inspired by images in the poems of Victor Hugo and by a photograph of the moon by Henry Fox-Talbot. The result is a dreamlike apparition of an eye-like moon that looks out at the night.

executed sketch inscribed *Troubled Dream*, in which the pose of the sleeper surrounded by terrifying apparitions is strikingly similar to that of the dreamer in Fuseli's *Nightmare*. The drawing stems from a period following the deaths of Sergel's friend and patron Gustavus Adolphus III and of his companion Anna Rella, during which the artist fell into a protracted period of despair and depression. In his autobiography he recalled that

in October 1795 I was afflicted with gout that spread to my intestines, with which I was ill for two years, and which attacked my nerves, provoking in me the most dreadful melancholy.

The drawing has been interpreted as a document of the relationship between artistic creation and madness. But the writhing shapes resembling serpents or birds that form a crescent around the sleeper, and the bones and skulls in front of his bed, need not signify madness, as the *philosophes* of the Enlightenment might have thought. Modern dream science suggests that such hallucinatory images are characteristic of dreams in general, regardless of their specific content.

Although the balance of dreams is tipped in the direction of the nightmare, it often swings, like the mood of a bipolar patient, to ecstatic mania. This is one of the reasons for the Romantics' fascination with dreams. At the beginning of the 19th century Maine de Biran distinguished between dreams in which "the most extraordinary inventions, the sublimest of thoughts" come to the mind of the dreamer, and "intuitive dreams or visions" in which the dreamer sees images of "phantoms of all colors and shapes."

DREAM ELATION AS ANTIDEPRESSANT

Ingres's Dream of Ossian in the Musée Ingres at Mantauban is the most ambitious early 19th-century depiction of the latter. The painting was commissioned for the ceiling of Napoleon's bedroom in the Palazzo Quirinale in Rome. Originally oval in format, the picture stayed on the ceiling of Napoleon's bedroom until 1836, when, at the request of Ingres, who was then director of the French Academy in Rome, it was sent to Paris and put in a square frame. The dreamer is the legendary 3rd-century Irish mystic poet Ossian, whose alleged works were published by James Macpherson in 1760-1763. Although they were at least in part, if not altogether, Macpherson's inventions, they had great appeal for the imagination of Romantic painters and poets, including Coleridge, who cited them in his notebooks. In Ingres' painting Malvina, the widow of Ossian's slain son Oscar, extends a comforting arm to the blind poet who has fallen asleep on a rock. Dream images of Nordic heroes whose deeds he celebrated in his epic poems appear above and behind him, rendered in ghostly, ectoplasmic grisaille tones. Ingres wrote three texts on the dream scenario of his paining. In the most concise he mused that

Ossian had only one son called Oscar; he gave him in marriage to Malvina; and after the death of his beloved son, in order to soothe the ennui of his old age and his blindness, he addressed the greater part of his poems to his widow. He has taken part in all the battles of which he sings. He has only his voice to console him. The memory of his misfortunes merges with the memory of his exploits. The past and the present overwhelm him.

Ossian's dream serves as both an escape from his present afflictions and as a connection to the heroic past celebrated in his poetry, just as Ingres and his contemporaries sought inspiration in the ideal beauty celebrated in classical art. The placement of Ingres' painting over Napoleon's bed constituted a potent dream-inducing stimulus to the

LE RÊVE

Victor Hugo, The Dream, 1853-1855, Maison de Victor Hugo, Paris.

Victor Hugo kept detailed records of his dreams, and filled an album with what he called "bizarre" dream drawings and watercolors. *The Dream* is an illustration of a couplet in one of his poems describing the apparition from an abyss of an alarming open hand.

emperor who sought to restore a sense of classical order to a world shaken by the violence of revolution.

SELF-OBSERVATION USING THE DREAM TELESCOPE

References to dreams and dreaming occur throughout the poems and novels of Victor Hugo. From 1856 on, Hugo's notebooks, like Coleridge's before him, contain detailed records of his dreams; and in his critical writings after 1862 Hugo reflected at length on the relationship between dreaming and creativity. Unlike Gérard de Nerval, who correctly viewed dreaming and waking as separate, though parallel states, Hugo regarded them as continuous, like light and dark, without a precise boundary where one ends and the other begins. In an essay *Promontorium somnii* (The Headland of the Dream) composed in 1863 he described a summit on the moon that he observed through a telescope in 1834 as a metaphor for the pinnacle of art:

In the mysterious world of art, as on the moon on which our gaze lighted just now, there is the summit of the dream.

Beginning in 1850 Hugo filled the pages of an album with what he called "bizarre" drawings and watercolors. They are related to his interest in spiritualism, which was intensified from the time of the death of his daughter in 1843. He began reading Pythagorean theory and the writings of Swedenborg; and in 1853 he was introduced to the doctrines of the Cabala by his friend Alexandre Weil. One of his "bizarre" drawings, entitled *The Dream*, illustrates a couplet from his poem *Les Thrones d'Orient* (The Thrones of the Orient):

Et on voyait sortir de l'abime insondable
Une sinistre main que s'ouvrait formidable.

(And one saw rising from the impenetrable abyss
A sinister hand which opened wondrously).

DRAWING ONE'S DREAMS: A PICTURE IS WORTH A THOUSAND WORDS

In 1862 Hugo's contemporary Alfred Maury (1817-1892) published a descriptive study of sleep and dreams, *Le sommeil et les rêves*, based on observation of his own dreams over an extended period of time. Maury was the first scientist who performed systematic experiments on his own sleep and dream states, and on the effects of external stimuli on dreaming. In order to control subjectivity and the loss of awareness experienced during sleep, Maury enlisted the help of accomplices who would periodically awaken him so that he would be able to have access to consciousness otherwise not recoverable.

Maury perceived the analogy between dreaming and delirium. Already a generation earlier Maine de Biran associated dreaming with delirium on the ground that in delirium, as in dreams, "that force which constitutes the person" has no influence on the imagination, and images take on their own vividness and depth. According to Maury, delirium is caused by the mind acting automatically and by a "perverse and irregular association of ideas," phenomena that also occur in dreams and which account for "the incoherence and the bizarre character of the ideas and images in them."

Maury was particularly interested in hypnagogic hallucinations, the visual images that are formed in the mind at sleep onset. He believed that the essential unit of any hallucinoid process consisted of a stimulus arising in the peripheral nervous system. When this stimulus reached the central nervous system, it triggered an illusion of a sensation; and the illusion, in turn, called forth a visual memory. By insisting on a sensory genesis for the hal-

Johan Tobias Sergel, *Troubled Dream*, 1795, Nationalmuseum, Stockholm.

The drawing stems from a period in which the artist fell into a protracted state of despair and depression, and has been interpreted as an example of the relationship between artistic creation and madness. Modern dream science has shown that the bones, skulls, and writhing forms surrounding the sleeper are triggered by the strong negative emotion experienced in dreams.

lucinosis of dreams, and attributing the defects and peculiarities of dreaming to a partial inactivation of brain function, Maury anticipated what has been scientifically demonstrated by modern dream science. But he was unaware of the fact that, as neuroscience has shown, the source of dream stimuli is within the brain itself.

Maury's contemporary Hervey de Saint-Denis filled twenty-two volumes with records and colored images representing five years of continuous self-experimentation and self-observation of his dreams. In Les rêves et les moyens de les diriger (1867) he demonstrated that it is possible for individuals to gain greater access to their own dreams simply by paying attention to them, either in "lucid dreaming" - when the dreamer is aware that he is dreaming - or in "controlled dreaming" - when the dreamer directs the course of his dreams. Like Maury, Hervey thought that dreaming was a replay of images stored in memory in a natural and spontaneous chain of reminiscences. Drawing on an analogy with the emerging technique of photography, he compared memory to a mirror covered with collodion, "which keeps continually and instantly the impression of images projected onto it by the lens of the dark chamber."

Hervey's response to dreaming was aesthetic. He believed that dreaming conveys artistic powers to every man; and he devoted more attention than anyone in recorded history to the visual nature of dreams. He was particularly interested in what he called "supersensual" dreams - the spontaneous, bizarre, and abstract dreams that occur at sleep onset, which differ from ordinary, well-formed, narrative dream scenarios.

The frontispiece of Hervey's book shown on page 178 depicts two kinds of visual imagery in sleep: the fully formed dream scenario, and the geometric, kaleidoscopic phantasms of sleep onset. Hervey ascribed the latter to retinal stimuli, but assumed that the former are somehow read out of memory. Whether or not either illustration is by his own hand we do not know. We do know, however, drawing was his preferred means of recording the visual, imagistic content of his dreams. In his notebook he drew fragmentary geometric figures like arabesques, and dots of color that appeared and disappeared over a web of fine threads of silver, gold, purple, and emerald green.

One of Hervey's descriptions of sleep-onset hypnagogic hallucinations illustrates their difference from dreams that occur later in the night:

A crystal green color takes shape in the center of my internal visual field. I make out, little by little, that it is a collection of leaves. It boils like a volcano about to erupt, it swells and expands rapidly owing to its moving forces. Red flowers come out of the crater and make an enormous bouquet. This remains clear for a minute then it all evaporates.

MODELS AND MECHANISMS: MIND AS COMPUTER AND CAMERA

Hervey was fascinated by the creativity of dreaming. He guessed but could not prove that it could be the product of hyperintensive activation of perception, of an increase of access to memories and to endogenous sources of stimulation, and of a decrease in stimulation from the outside world. He did not imagine that the brain itself might be the source of dream stimulation. He was critical of contemporary French psychology, which he chastised for ignoring some of the most interesting and informative aspects of subjective experience. The fact that his own theory of dream formation was significantly influenced by the advent of photography helps us to understand the limitations of his conceptualizations. Not unlike Grandville, Hervey thought of dream images as a series of *clichés souvenirs*, or memory snapshots, played back in cinema-like fashion on the screen of the dreaming mind.

Arthur Schopenhauer (1788-1860) in *Versuch über das Geistersehen* (On Apparitions), published in 1862, took the position that while we are awake external stimuli impinge upon the mind and cause it to erect models of time, space, and causality in relation to the realities of the external world, while internal stimuli have relatively little importance. During sleep, however, the sources of external stimulation markedly diminish, allowing the ratio of internal to external stimulation to rise. In dreams, Schopenhauer concluded, internal stimuli are remodeled into forms occupying space and time by rules unique to the brain itself.

Hermann von Helmholtz, the father of modern physiology and psychophysiology, conjectured in *Sensations of Tone* (1863) that the brain commands movement in dreaming, and this gives rise to sensory images. The evidence of neurological research has confirmed Helmholtz's assumption that movements in dreaming have a neuronal basis in the brain. In chapter 2 we described the waves of neuronal activation that arise in the brain stem and radiate to the visual brain in the thalamus and the cortex. Because these so-called PGO waves encode eye movement in REM sleep, we speculated that they could provide information used in visual image construction during dreaming. We follow Helmholtz's suggestion that motor intentions give rise to signals that allow the visual sensory system to cope with changes in eye position. Following Schopenhauer, we have also suggested that the rise during REM sleep in the ratio of internal to external stimulus strength is driven by the increased excitability of the PGO system, and by the active exclusion of external stimuli.

Eye Movement and Dream Vision

Until not long ago these ideas rested solely on data from animal experiments because efforts to record PGO waves in humans had been unsuccessful. Recently, however, PET imaging has changed this picture by showing that both the visual thalamus and the visual cortex are more active in REM sleep when eye movement is intense than when it is quiescent. While this does not prove that the eye movement related increase in visual sensory areas is mediated by PGO waves, it does show that the visual motor and visual sensory systems are functionally linked.

Helmholtz's most distinguished student Wilhelm Wundt (1832-1920), the founder of the first laboratory devoted to physiological psychology, was convinced that the psychology of dreaming must derive from the physiology of the brain in sleep. Noting that dreaming is characterized by both deficits (the impairment of logic, memory, and judgment) and enhancements (the intensification of associations, visual imagery, and emotion), Wundt correctly surmised that in sleep some brain structures would show decreases and other increases in their activity. Assuming that a mind state will have a corresponding brain state, he predicted that if the mind state

of dreams is characterized by heightened sensations and decreased volition, physiological research would one day reveal an increase in activity in the brain's sensory centers and a decrease in nervous centers related to volition or attention, a prediction that modern neurophysiology has abundantly corroborated by the recent spate of imaging studies that we have described.

By putting the study of dreams on a scientific basis, Wundt, Helmholtz, Schopenhauer, Hervey de Saint-Denis, and Maury were the precursors of the modern science of dreaming. Like neurophysiologists today, though without modern laboratory technology for experimentally testing their hypotheses, they were interested in the formal structure and mechanism of dreams. Until recently, however, these interests have been overshadowed by Freud's exclusive emphasis on the latent dream content from which the so-called manifest dream is derived in disguised form. It is the manifest dream, however, that is the subject of the theory and depiction of dreams in the late 18th and 19th centuries, and that is also the subject of the neurological study of dreams today. For us, the dream is the dream is the dream.

Freud too had initially wanted to follow this path. In his *Project for a Scientific Psychology* (1895) he wrote that if psychology was to be free from doubt it must be rooted in brain science. He therefore attempted to construct a theory of the mind utilizing the newly formulated neurone doctrine of Santiago Ramon y Cajal, the discovery that the brain functions by means of communication systems among billions of individual, discrete neurones, or nerve cells. But because nothing was known at the time about the neurophysiology of sleep or mental illness, Freud abandoned his Project and shifted to a purely psychological approach. The result was *The Interpretation of Dreams*, which portrayed dreams as disguised manifestations of repressed unconscious wishes.

Many scientists have been skeptical of Freud's claims. But until the publication in the activation-synthesis hypothesis in 1977, there was no coherent alternative theory. Because Freud's theory of dreams rested on a neurological model which postulated that all the energy within the nervous system comes from external sources, and none from internal ones, Freud thought of the nervous system exclusively in terms of reflex actions, as a system operating only when driven by external forces and incapable of creating its own actions.

It is ironic that three years after the publication of *The Interpretation of Dreams*, the French psychiatrist Henri Beaunis (1830-1921) published an observational study in the *American Journal of Psychology* in which he advanced the idea that all mental activity reflects brain physiology. Beaunis made careful and astute observations of his own dreams, and compared their formal qualities to his waking thoughts. He noted that dream content was determined as much by intrinsic factors as by the nature and quantity of previous experience; and he concluded that dreaming is the synthesis of images and information generated by the activation of the brain in sleep. Though as yet unsupported by experimental data, the fundamental axioms of the activation-synthesis hypothesis were available to Freud, had he wanted to make use of them.

DARKNESS BREEDS DREAMING: FROM BLACK AND WHITE TO COLOR

The artistic counterpart to the scientific study of dreams in the second half of the 19th century is the work of the French painter and graphic artist Odilon Redon (1840-1916). In a series of autobiographical sketches published in 1909 Redon wrote that nature prescribes "obedience to the gifts which it endowed us. Mine has induced me to

dreams." Redon's friend Paul Gauguin recognized this gift when some twenty years earlier he wrote that Redon is

a dreamer, a visionary... Nature has mysterious powers of imagination... The artist himself is one of nature's means, and, to me, Redon is one of those chosen for the continuation of its creations. His dreams become reality through the probability that he gives them.

In his autobiographical memoir *À soi-même* Redon gives a detailed account of his childhood in the dark, large, isolated house in the wine country near Bordeaux, and of the flowering of his visual imagination in that shuttered setting. As in the modular behavior of the brain in REM sleep, a reduction in external stimuli is often associated with a reciprocal increase in internal ones, especially in subjects whose brains are biased towards image production. Such susceptibility may predispose persons to hypnotisability and psychosis, or, as in Redon's case, to produce hypnopsychotic art that is eminently sane.

Until 1889 Redon worked primarily in black and white. He published his first album of lithographs, *Dans le rêve* (In the Dream), in 1879. In a letter of July 21, 1898 to his friend André Mellerio, who was cataloguing his prints, drawings, and paintings, Redon wrote that among his albums *Dans le rêve*

is perhaps one of my favorites, because it has been made without any literary component; the title Dans le rêve being in some way no more than a key to it (une clef d'ouverture).

The lithograph entitled *Vision* was inspired by a photograph of the moon by Henry Fox-Talbot, and by images in poems by Victor Hugo of the dream-like apparition of the ominous eyes of the moon and of the celestial globe turning into an enormous eye that looks out at the night. Other composi-

Odilon Redon, The Dream, 1904, Collection Claude Blancpain, Fribourg.

An embryonic, protohuman vapor trail rises toward the light from a red spot of activation embedded in darkness. Although

Redon could not know that the red spot represents the pontine brain stem, and that dreams emerge from the autoactivation of the

sleeping brain, the painting clearly suggests the autocreative capacity of the brain in the dream state.

tions in *Dans le Rêve*, such as Germination, depict dreaming as a germinal life process in a cosmogenic space, inspired by studies that Redon made together with his teacher Rudolf Bresdin of microscopic life in drops of pond water.

The fact that Redon's dream lithographs are black-and-white should not necessarily be taken to suggest that his dream visions lacked color. Modern sleep science has demonstrated that as laboratory reports become longer, they increasingly describe vividly perceived colors, suggesting that it is poor dream recall that is at the root of the popular belief that dream vision is colorless. Following Redon's encounter in 1889 with the art of the Symbolist painters Maurice Denis and Paul Serusier, effulgent, luxurious color broke through in his work.

In Redon's painting *The Dream*, an embryonic, protohuman vapor trail rises toward the light from a red spot of activation embedded in darkness. Although the painting is entirely abstract, the sense of an internal source of illumination for the dream is clearly expressed. Redon did not know that the red spot represents the pontine brain stem, and that dreams emerged from the autoactivation of the sleeping brain. Nevertheless, he came remarkably close to depicting the autocreative capacity of the brain in the dream state.

At the turn of the 20th century a number of modernist artists were drawn to dreaming as a mental state that could inform their analysis of internal vision, and directly enhance access to this inner, spiritual vision in the service of the imagination and the creative process. It was one of the roads the led them to abstraction. The same qualities that liberated artists in quest of what John Golding has called "paths to absolute," were not equally helpful to modern dream science, whose progress was delayed by half a century by the psychological approach to dreaming of psychoanalysis, and the slow development of electronic technology that allowed the abstracting capacities of the brain to be visualized.

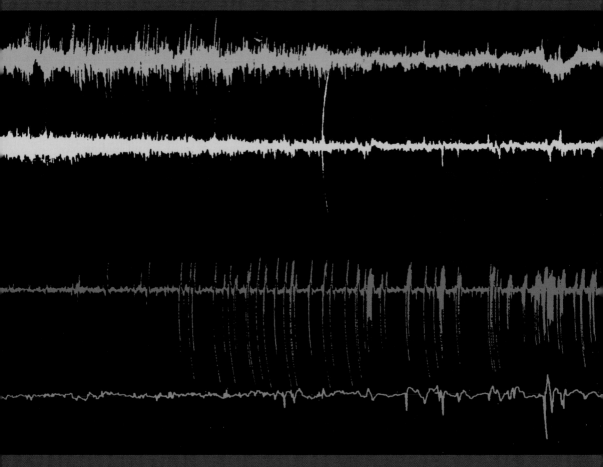

REM Sleep Onset.

When REM sleep begins there is a progressive and simultaneous brain activation (orange) and muscle tone suppression (yellow). The activation of the brain induces eye movement (green) and PGO waves in the visual thalamus itself (purple). This complex but coordinated set of processes turns the brain on (orange) and turns motor output off (yellow) eccept for the eyes (green). Information about the eye movement (purple) is generated and transmitted within the brain itself.

Inner Space

Brain Science, Dreaming and Modern Art

The author has tried to imitate the disconnected but
apparently logical form of a dream.
Everything can happen;
everything is possible and likely.
Time and space do not exist; on an insignificant
basis of reality, the imagination spins and weaves
new patterns: a blending of memories, experiences,
free inventions, absurdities, and improvisations.
The characters are split, double, redouble, evaporate,
condense, scatter and converge.
But one consciousness remains above all of them: the
dreamer's; for him there are no secrets,
no inconsequences, no scruples, no law.
He does not judge, does not acquit, simply relates.

August Strindberg, *Preface to A Dream Play (1901)*

One of the characteristics of the modern spirit in science and art is to probe beneath the surface appearances of phenomena to the structures and mechanisms that underlie them. Stimulated by Freud's bold assertions of the formative role of the unconscious in mental life and by scientific innovations, such as the discovery of X-rays, artists began depicting unconscious processes that they imagined underlay our states of consciousness. In this chapter we look at examples of this shared impulse to delve beneath the surface by focusing on the interest in sleep and dreams of both artists and scientists, especially in the work of those who, like Strindberg, have espoused the formal approach to dreaming that has proved so fruitful in dream science.

Fascination with the unseen reveals itself in science in the paradigm shift that began in the late nineteenth century with Darwin's *Origin of Species* (1859), through which biology was dynamically reconstructed: all life forms were seen to be the product of invisible structures, the genes which have since been shown to be complex but precisely specifiable molecules. The recent announcement of the complete analysis of the human genome brings to a close this dramatic 20th-century chapter of scientific research.

The corresponding paradigm shift to modernism in art arose from the poetic and intuitive Romantic/Symbolist poetic in the unseen forces that organize nature, including human nature, and the analytical/experimental willingness to fracture the surface of things. The fragmented, discontinuous brushstrokes of Cézanne and the dots of color that make up the paintings of Seurat may be seen as artistic responses to the hypothesis of Max Planck that the physical world consists of randomly organized atoms and molecules, and to the premise formulated by Hermann von Helmholtz in the middle of the 19th century that the perception of visual imagery is a construction of the brain.

Cubism developed this premise further by examining objects from several points of view at once; while Surrealism attempted to give form to images arising from the vast, invisible repository of the unconscious mind.

The link between these methods and objectives in the domain of art to what was going on in science, especially in the brain and mind sciences, was not only a function of a common intellectual and cultural climate. It was also explicit and direct. Like Cézanne and Seurat, for example, neurophysiology was dedicated to understanding how the continuous and integral visual image of our perception could be built up from the atomistic elements employed by neurones to encode the visual world in terms of edges and colors. Gestalt psychology, like Cubism, focused on how wholes were sought in complex stimulus patterns and how the mind could choose one image over another when presented with ambiguous overlapping and incompatible stimuli. Like Surrealism, psychoanalytic psychology was persuaded that the conscious mind was a compromised cover-up for an instinctually demanding unconscious whose existence and fundamentally formative nature could best be understood by paying attention to dreams and other mental automatisms that reflected the force of unconscious drives relatively directly.

In both science and art, form had priority over content, and the particular image or datum was designed (in the case of art) or analyzed (in the case of science) to test a hypothesis of how the general leads to the specific. In this project both science and art adopted reductionistic strategies. Here reductionism is defined as the attempt to explain the largest number of variables with the smallest number of assumptions. This shared strategy led to the adoption, in both art and science, of abstract models and of representations of those models in operation. Abstraction in both art and science is essentially the selection of those factors deemed most relevant to establishing and understanding the structures underlying a complex surface reality. Modern science and art were both dedicated to the formulation of general rules about how the world is constructed and how we see it. This is true whether we are considering a sculpture by Naum Gabo or a mathematical formula like Ludwig Boltzmann's proof of the second law of thermodynamics. Both are abstract. Both are models. And both are beautiful in their simple rendering of complex structures.

AT THE TURN OF THE CENTURY

If we were asked to identify the time frame in which the psychological and neurophysiological study of the brain/mind took on its current "modern" form it would be the decade between 1890 and 1900. In that decade three important developments set the science of sleep and dreaming on its current course.

The first was the publication in 1890 of William James' *Principles of Psychology* which began with a chapter of what was then known about the brain and declared that brain science was fundamental to psychology in all of its aspects including the transcendent, the spiritual and the supernatural. Its sequel, *Varieties of Religious Experience*, published in 1912, made the same points even more emphatically and offered examples from a wide variety of sources. James was avowedly agnostic and determinedly open about such numinous agencies as extrasensory perception, communication with the dead, and, we might suppose, even angels.

The second was the completion in 1895 of the unpublished *Project for a Scientific Psychology* in which Sigmund Freud attempted to construct a theory of the mind that could account for the unseen dynamics of uncon-

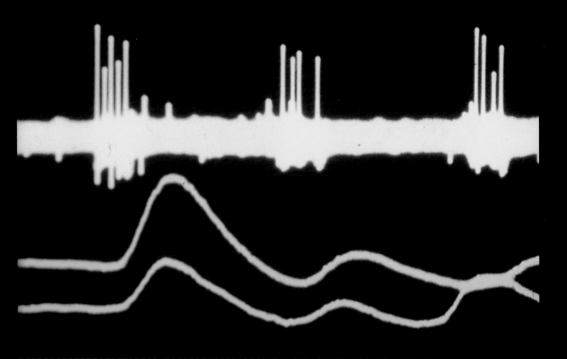

PGO Cells.

As we lie asleep in our beds and our eyes move to the right or left, our •

brains process movement associated signals. This is dramatically true of the thalamic relay nucleus (called the lateral

geniculate body) and the posterolateral cortex where visual perception is thought to occur. The cell fires a burst (upper trace)

prior to both larger (same side) and smaller (opposite side) waves in the visual thalamus (lower traces).

scious processes on the basis of neurones and their physiology. Freud's imaginative synthetic effort was thwarted because he lacked the neurophysiological data to support his ambition. Although he set his Project aside, the ideas that it contained resurfaced in the theory of dreams as the disguised form of unfulfilled wishes arising from the unconscious, published in 1900. Freud had finished *The Interpretation of Dreams* a year earlier but delayed its appearance to make it a clarion call to the opening of the 20th century.

The third signal event was the elaboration of the Neurone Doctrine by the Spanish neuro-anatomist Santiago Ramon y Cajal. In its emphasis on the discreteness of neurones as the structural units of the brain, Cajal's

work provided the paradigm that has guided neuroscience successfully for a century. Now that it is combined with the genetic model, it seems likely to continue to be germinal for at least another 100 years. Ramon y Cajal was much more than a journeyman anatomist. He was also a psychologist who, like Freud, was fascinated by the effects of hypnosis. Moreover, he was an accomplished draftsman who made all of the pen-and-ink renderings of neurones that illustrate his papers and books. Although photography was available to him, Cajal insisted that his students take art lessons to learn how to become more active analytic observers.

These three epochal events have shaped modern science in ways that are crucial to

Giorgio de Chirico, Song of Love, 1914, The Museum of Modern Art, New York.

De Chirico aspired to making pictures in which sense and logic would be missing, as they are during sleep, and thus come close to the dream state. The classical head and the rubber glove, for example, are both body parts, but they are inanimate and discontinuous, and could not be connected to an animate body.

our story. James set the stage for the physiological emphasis in 20th-century experimental psychology. Freud, by calling attention to dreaming as a psychological model for understanding the unconscious mind in terms of its neurobiological underpinnings, foreshadowed the integrative models that can now be constructed and tested. The goals of his Project for a Scientific Psychology are finally within our grasp. And by correctly discerning the exquisite microscopic design of the brain, Ramon y Cajal created the approach now used to unify the experimental psychology of dreaming with basic neurobiology.

Summarizing the findings and models that we have discussed in chapters 1 and 2, we can now approach dreaming, that most numinous of mental states, ascribed for centuries to external agencies like angels, as the product of shifts in brain chemistry. A new understanding of the creation and experience of art, grounded in what neurophysiology has shown of the autocreativity and the synthetic coalescence of perception, emotion and memory in the brain/mind, is close at hand. We will now examine some of the key steps in its development.

Psychoanalysis and Surrealism

Freud's theory of dreaming was embraced by psychologists and artists alike, none more than André Breton, the theoretician of Surrealism who had studied psychiatry with Charcôt at the Salpetrière in Paris. However, as A. Alvarez has pointed out, Breton and the Surrealists were less interested in mental life as it reveals itself in dreams than in dreaming's uncanny and disjointed juxtapositions, its bizarreness, and its hallucinoid visual processes. Breton and the Surrealists failed to grasp Freud's main point about dreams and the unconscious: that instead of revealing the truth they conceal it. By concentrating on the manifest dream, rather than on the latent dream content that the manifest dream expresses in disguised, symbolic form, they were remarkably successful in describing dreaming's formal qualities, as we shall see especially clearly in works by Giorgio de Chirico, Salvador Dali, Max Ernst, and René Magritte.

Giorgio de Chirico and the Celebration of Decortication

The supreme early twentieth-century master of visionary dream pictures was Giorgio de Chirico. *Soothsayer's Return*, in the Philadelphia Museum of Art, is one of several paintings de Chirico made in Paris between 1911 and 1915 of architectural piazzas, deserted but for an antique statue of the Sleeping Ariadne. The deliberately crude brushwork in the rendering of the antique statue, leaving it ambiguous whether she is an inert statue or a restless sleeper, and her placement, in a spectrally lit, empty setting before a modern railway station at 1:56 in the afternoon, come close, as de Chirico put it, to the hallucinatory intensity, the incongruity and irrationality of the dream state.

De Chirico was profoundly influenced by Schopenhauer's essay "On Apparitions" (*Versuch über das Geistersehn*) in which, as Nietzsche wrote in *The Birth of Tragedy*,

Schopenhauer actually designates the gift of occasionally regarding men and things as mere phantoms and dream pictures as the criterion of philosophical ability.

De Chirico clearly possessed this gift. He wrote that,

A truly immortal work of art can only be born through revelation...; to be really immortal a work of art must go completely beyond the lim-

Max Klinger, Akkorde, 1894, Museum der bildenden Kunst, Leipzig.

In its emotional consilience of incongruity and discontinuity Klinger's etching corresponds, as virtually no earlier depiction of a dream scenario, to the formal characteristics of dreams identified by nineteenth-century writers and corroborated by modern dream science.

its of the human; good sense and logic will be missing from it. In this way it will come close to the dream state, and also to the mentality of children.

What both adult dreamers and children lack, as the basis of their deficient good sense and logic, is the function of their frontal lobes, especially the dorsolateral prefrontal cortex. This structure develops late in humans - witness the behavior of most adolescents and many young adults - and may degenerate early, as in the pre-senile dementia of the fifth decade, if it is not severed from the rest of the brain by pre-frontal lobotomy. But we can all achieve de Chirico's criterion for an immortal work of art simply by going to sleep. When we enter REM sleep the brain activation (which is otherwise widespread) spares this region, so that in our dreams it is guaranteed that good sense and logic will be missing.

Good sense and logic depend upon the dorsolateral prefrontal cortex because it is the brain's seat of working memory. By working memory we mean the current occupants of that small, constantly changing mental space into which we put our intentions and thoughts so as to organize and direct our behavior deliberately in waking. Self-reflective awareness, critical judgment, directed thought, and decisive action all depend upon working memory. Without it, we are adrift in a sea of perceptions, feelings, and ad hoc explanations.

What de Chirico is telling us is that there is another natural state in which we can achieve his goal, in a neurophysiological sense, of functional decortication. That state is dreaming. In *Song of Love* in the Museum of Modern Art in New York de Chirico illustrates this by the juxtaposition of elements that have a set of useful cognitive conjunctions, though not the usual ones. The head of the *Apollo Belvedere* and the rubber glove are both body parts, but they are inanimate and discontinuous. They are not and could not be connected in an intact body. Likewise, the objects and architecture - a sphere, a building suggesting a Renaissance portico, a slab behind the glove and the classical head, a brick wall, and behind it a locomotive - are discontinuous in respect to scale, historical style, and use. The head of the *Apollo Belvedere*, an allusion to poetry and clairvoyance, was copied from a book on classical art by the French archaeologist Salomon Reinach. The locomotive alludes to the artist's childhood (his father was a railroad engineer). The Renaissance portico is an allusion to de Chirico's fascination with arcades. The arcade, he wrote in one of his journals, "is a fatality. Its voice speaks in riddles filled with a strange Roman poetry."

By using our frontal lobes we can, in the light of day, see that de Chirico has simply loosened the criteria for associating objects, body parts, and historical epochs, and put them together synthetically, just as dreams do when their brain representations are activated in sleep. Memories, as stored in the brain, are retrievable according to many different associative rules. No matter what the particular context may demand, body parts like heads and gloves go together in one category; walls, arches, and spheres in another; trains and gloves and classical fragments in still others. We can thus credit de Chirico not only with an accurate reading of the formal properties of dreams, but also with an inadvertent anticipation of dream function: to reinforce loosely connected but important cognitive categories that constitute that rich set of associative options that we need to function while awake. What is missing from de Chirico's formulation is emotional salience. His paintings are so strange as to evoke dreamlike anxiety in the waking observer.

The data of modern dream science suggest that disorientation and anxiety are inherent, independently generated aspects of the dreaming brain, which is as disconnected from its moorings in the outside world as the viewer of de Chirico's painting. For us, dream anxiety is not a symptom or a defense, as Freud thought, but an existential given. De Chirico appears to have intuitively understood that when dream anxiety interacts with dream disorientation, both are intensified.

DREAMLIKE REALITY OR PSYCHOANALYTIC FANTASY?

Among the artists whom de Chirico admired, and the one whose works come closest to the "dream state" to which de Chirico himself aspired was the Viennese sculptor and painter Max Klinger. In 1894 Klinger made an etching with the musical title *Akkorde* for the frontispiece of *Brahmsphantasie*, the artist's homage to Johannes Brahms. Like Goya's *El sueño de la razon produce monstruous* two centuries earlier, *Akkorde* is an innovative dream picture in that the bizarreness, incongruity, and discontinuity of its imagery correspond, as in virtually no earlier depiction of a dreamlike scenario, to the formal characteristics of dreams gleaned by nineteenth-century scientists and corroborated by modern dream science.

The fact that the essential forms taken by dream bizarreness are incongruity and discontinuity has led us to suggest that the dreaming brain, like the imagery of Klinger's engraving, has lost its orientational stability. The Aristotelean unities of time, place, and action are exploded with dramatic effect. The incongruously juxtaposed seascape, harpist, and pianistic duo are bound together, as in a dream - and like the thematic, harmonic, and rhythmic material in music - by the unifying power of movement, turbulence, and emotional intensity. The one component of dreams that is never incongruous is emotion. Emotion infuses each of the cognitive aspects of dreaming even when they are incongruous among themselves. The deep meaning of *Akkorde* arises from its emotional, dreamlike consilience of incongruity and discontinuity.

This quality of Klinger's etching made a deep, lasting impression on de Chirico, who recognized in Klinger a kindred spirit, with the aspiration of making pictures which, as de Chirico put it, "will come close to the dream state." In his obituary of Klinger in 1920 de Chirico wrote that he

often combines in the same composition scenes of contemporary life and antique visions, thus producing a dreamlike reality. In order to make the scenario in Akkorde even more realistic, Klinger has placed next to the piano a wooden ladder like those in the cabins of bathing establishments, whose lower steps descend into the water. The idea of this ladder is extraordinarily ingenious. It unites the real and the unreal scenarios, rendering one in the same way as the other, not hazily and confusedly, as some painters have done in compositions with unreal components. If the pianist were to quit his instrument, he could climb down into the water, just as the marine creatures, were they to climb up the ladder, could sit down on the stage. It is a dream at the same time as it is real, like a scenario we

have seen before, without being able to remember when or where.

De Chirico's description of the composition is an admirably accurate characterization not only of Klinger's etching, but, by extension, of the imagery of dreaming consciousness in general. It set the tone for the exploration of the relationship between oneiric and artistic imagery in a wide variety of media that is one of the distinctive, innovative features of the art of the 20th century.

Like the 12th-century illuminator of the *Dream of Jacob* in the Lambeth Bible (who used the image of the ladder as the link between the realm of man and the realm of God) Klinger employed it as the means of mediating the transition from the waking state to the dream world. But now, instead of angels descending from heaven with messages from God, the dreamer himself can descend the ladder to the primordial underworld. Moreover, Klinger's ladder is a two-way street, allowing the inhabitants of the oneiric underworld to ascend to the higher world of waking. This double transformation, from marine creatures to man and vice versa, and from waking to dreaming and back, has phylogenetic and Darwinian overtones as well as cerebral equivalency. The marine creatures may advance, as it were, via an evolutionary ladder, and thereby achieve the higher order of humanity, an evolutionary process that would require a change in brain state and a corresponding evolution of the brain.

Marine creatures do not have either the brain structures or the internal activation of the brain necessary for dreaming. They have no REM and they lack the thalamus and cortex and the REM process that converts Klinger's sea creatures to Klinger's pianist. Evolution provides the brain with more than the simply additive capability of new structures. It also confers new capabilities upon

Max Ernst, *Pietà ou la Revolution la Nuit, 1923, Tate Britain, London.*

Whether or not it represents an actual dream, the picture adopts the Surrealist strategy, as dreams do, of inverting and transgressing normal categories and expectation, such as the replacement of the grieving mother in the Christian Pietà by an impassive, brutal father; and the substitution of the dead Christ with a catatonic patient dressed in the white smock worn by patients at the Salpetrière.

existing structures. Thus the brainstem of man is not the brainstem of the fish. The evolution of the thalamo-cortical system is paralleled by an evolution of the brainstem. Thus the change in state from waking to dreaming does not represent a regression from a more evolved state to a more primodial one. Both waking and REM sleep, like the human cortex and brainstem, are highly evolved states, each with its own highly evolved purpose.

Dreaming as a Nocturnal Revolution: Max Ernst and Psychoanalysis

The pictures that de Chirico produced in Paris between 1911 and 1915 made a deep impression on the Surrealists, especially on Max Ernst. In Ernst's *Pietà ou la Revolution la Nuit* painted in Paris in 1923, the middle-aged man with a mustache and lowered eyes is an allusion to de Chirico's *The Child's Brain* in the Moderna Museet in Stockholm. This memory image of his father was painted at the time when de Chirico wrote that art should "come close to the dream state and also to the mentality of children". In 1919 André Breton, profoundly moved by the work's "exceptional ability to shock," had acquired it for his collection, and Ernst knew it well from visits to Breton's apartment at 42 Rue Fontaine.

The reference to *The Child's Brain* in Ernst's picture is one of many allusions to de Chirico in his work. David Sylvester pointed out that

the girl running in Ernst's Two Children are Threatened by a Nightingale (1924) in the Museum of Modern Art is meant to be read as the front view of the running girl seen from the back in [de] Chirico's Mystery and Melancholy of a Street (1914)...When Ernst borrows, his audience is clearly meant to recognize the source...[If]

the allusion is missed at the time we look at the work, so is some of the point of the work.

Both de Chirico and Ernst subscribed to the idea that dreaming was a way of recapturing the mind of the child and of recovering lost truths that are buried in that mind. From our formal point of view, it is true that the functional decortication of REM sleep makes the dreaming mind comparable to the mind of an undeveloped child or a degenerate adult. But only comparable. Not identical. To help make this point clear consider the memory issues involved. If we take the notion of dreaming as regression to an earlier state literally we could reasonably expect to recover apparently lost childhood experiences. But since all the evidence suggests that many early childhood memories, like most of our unremembered dreams, are simply gone forever, fishing for them in dreams is a fool's errand. Max Ernst helps us understand this error in relation to other borrowings from psychoanalysis and from André Breton's own agenda.

Pietà ou la Revolution la Nuit is a dream picture whether or not it represents a dream, but because it works the way a dream does. The middle-aged man is Philip Ernst, the artist's father. The figure he is holding is his son in the form of a mannequin, a favorite Surrealist image, rendered in flat shapes, like a cut-out, with the uniformly gray head of a classical statue, perhaps a reference to classical heads in paintings by de Chirico, such as the head of the *Apollo Belvedere* in *Song of Love*. In other respects as well, Ernst employs the Surrealist strategy of inverting and transgressing normal categories and expectations, a device advocated by Breton, and a characteristic feature of the experience of dreams.

The most obvious inversion is Ernst's replacement of the grieving mother in the Christian image of the Pietà with the impassive, brutal father. Another is the substitution of the limp, stretched-out pose of the son by the rigid, upright, angular pose of a catatonic patient dressed in the white smock worn by patients at Salpetrière. According to Emil Kraepelin's *Dementia Praecox und Paraphrenia* (1919), catatonic patients "let themselves be... lifted up in the air like a parcel... without changing the position of their limbs in any way," and their facial expression is "vacant, immobile, [and] like a mask."

The image of the father has been connected with an account that Ernst wrote in 1927 of a daydream that he recalled having between the ages of five and seven and then remembering as an adolescent. In the dream a man with the mustache of his father made comical, obscene gestures and wielded a whip

with all his force, [accompanying] his movements with terrible gasps of breath, comparable to the snorts of an enormous and enraged steam engine...One day, at the age of puberty, in examining the question of how my father had conducted himself in the night of my conception, there arose in me, as if in response to this question of filial respect, precise and irrefutable, the memory of that vision of half-sleep that I had forgotten.

The connection of the dream to *Pietà ou la Revolution la Nuit* is problematic. Ernst did not report his dream and how he happened to remember it until four years after he had painted the picture; moreover, his description of the dream, of which we have cited only a short excerpt, is so overloaded with obvious Freudian symbols that one wonders to what extent he elaborated or even invented it. That he could have invented it is made clear by the recent discoveries of cognitive psychologists demonstrating the ease with which highly detailed but entirely false memories can be implanted in unsuspecting children and psychotherapeutically committed adults. Freud himself was so aware of the power of this kind of suggestion that he vig-

orously distanced himself from hypnosis, and refused to touch or even look face to face at his patients for fear of making unwanted suggestions to them.

FREUD MEETS BRETON AND POLITELY REJECTS HIM

Freud had little sympathy for Surrealism. André Breton reported that on his visit to Freud at Bergstrasse 19 on October 9, 1921 he tried

to make him talk by throwing names such as Charcôt and Babinsky into the conversation, but either because the memories I'm calling upon are too distant or because he maintains a posture of cautious reticence with strangers, I can only get him to speak in generalities.

The poetic, dreamlike imagery of Surrealist painting and literature held no meaning for Freud. On December 8, 1937 he wrote to Breton that

the superficial aspect of dreams, what I call the manifest dream, holds no interest for me. I have been concerned with the "latent content" which can be derived from the manifest dream by psychoanalytic interpretation. A collection of dreams without associations and knowledge of the context in which it was dreamed does not tell me anything, and it is hard for me to imagine what it can mean to anyone else.

SECOND THOUGHTS: BACK TO THE FUTURE AND THE FORM OF DREAMS

Toward the end of his life Freud had second thoughts about Surrealism. After Stefan Zweig had brought Salvador Dali to visit him at 20 Marefield Gardens in London on July 19, 1939, two months before his death,

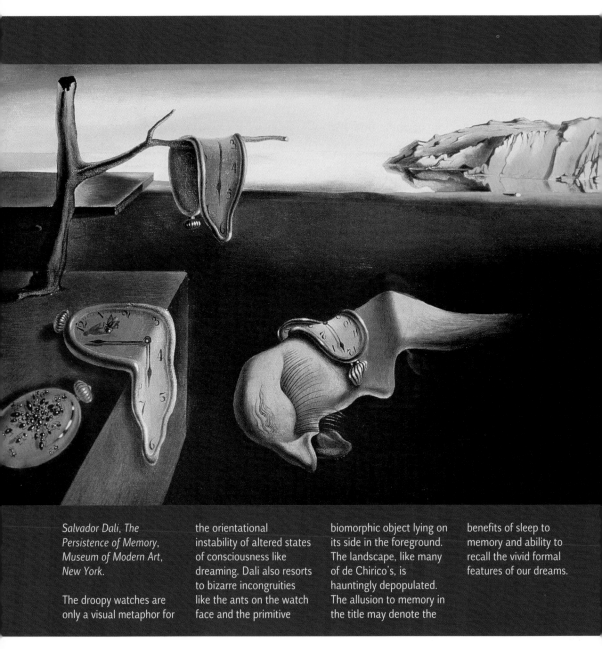

Salvador Dali, *The Persistence of Memory*, Museum of Modern Art, New York.

The droopy watches are only a visual metaphor for the orientational instability of altered states of consciousness like dreaming. Dali also resorts to bizarre incongruities like the ants on the watch face and the primitive biomorphic object lying on its side in the foreground. The landscape, like many of de Chirico's, is hauntingly depopulated. The allusion to memory in the title may denote the benefits of sleep to memory and ability to recall the vivid formal features of our dreams.

Freud wrote to Zweig:

I really owe you thanks for bringing yesterday's visitor. For until now I have been inclined to regard the Surrealists, who have apparently chosen me for their patron saint, as absolute (let us say 95 per cent, like alcohol) cranks. The young Spaniard, however, with his candid fanatical eyes and his undeniable technical mas-tery, has made me reconsider my opinion.

Whatever Freud's revised opinion of the Surrealists may have been, they rarely, if ever, made pictures of actual dreams. The temptation to think that they did arises from the fact that their pictures often work in the same way as dreams do. The art historian Robert Goldwater thought that the soft watches in Salvador Dali's *Persistence of Memory* in the Museum of Modern Art in New York are "learned references to a vocabulary of dreams." While this may be true in so far as the drooping watches in the picture suggest the fluidity of time and the disorientation in relation to time that we experience in dreams, the painting is a classic example of what David Sylvester has called the Surrealist strategy of showing objects "behaving contrary to their nature." The Surrealists, according to Sylvester, used dreams not as expressions or reflections of unconscious fantasies but as a visual language, a way of transforming memory, desire, apprehension, or panic into images. It is a visual language that we intuitively recognize and respond to. In reference to our capacity to do so Ludwig Wittgenstein said that

there seems to be something in dream images that has a certain resemblance to the signs of a language. As a series of marks on paper or sand might have. There might be no mark which we recognize as a conventional sign in any alphabet we knew, and yet we might have a strong feeling that they must be a language of some sort: that they mean something.

Is this what Dali's *Persistence of Memory* is trying to tell us in the image of soft, seemingly melting watches? That time, one of the main orientational anchors of waking consciousness, is altered in dreams as part of the price paid for its own functional reorganization? That we are rewinding our memory clocks at the same time that our brain clocks are telling us not to concern ourselves about time in our dreams?

Among 20th-century painters, Salvador Dali, for all his exhibitionism, gave visual form to certain aspects of dreaming with remarkable astuteness and accuracy. Consider, for example, the specificity of his didactic tour de force, *Dream Caused by the Flight of a Bee Around a Pomegranate One Second Before Awakening* in the Museo Thyssen-Bornemisza in Madrid. In the tradition of Grandville, Dali maps the successive transformation of visual dream images and adds the attendant emotions of anger, fear, and helplessness in a seamless synthesis. From a dream stimulus (the buzzing of a tiny neurone-like insect) just below the brainstem of his gloriously nude dreamer to her penetration by a microelectrode-like bayonet well aimed at the stimulus source of her dream, Dali traces the metamorphosis of the image. The pomegranate explodes. From its surface emerges a marine creature which vomits the two fierce tigers whose claws become the rifle's bayonet. The long-legged elephant walking with stilt-like strides across the desolate dream landscape is an unexplained incongruity. The rocky slabs over which the dreaming nude floats add to the sense of physical impossibility and menace that leads to the awakening promised in the title.

We hasten to assure the reader that the bee as neurone and the bayonet as microelectrode are our own scientifically derived metaphors. They are not to be taken literally; they are, rather, reminders of our own dream hypothesis and its naturalistic data base. And yet: the bee is explicitly taken as the inciting stimulus, whether Dali thought it was buzzing outside or only in the dreamer's mind. Even if it was only a figment of his own imagination, it is significant that it is a very small, entirely natural life process that gets a dream going. What gets the dream stopping is the typically hot affect, the fear that so overactivates the brain as to break the input-output gates as wide open as the exploding pomegranate. Dream sequences that are as well remembered as this one is represented typically follow sudden awakenings engendered by fear of nightmarish intensity. Such awakenings also typically occur from REM sleep after an intense burst of REMs that is associated with the physical con-

Pablo Picasso, Youth and Sleeping Girl, 1931, Private Collection.

Picasso's drawing of the sleeping girl and the watching youth records the reciprocity of sleeping and waking as interdependent states of consciousness, the latter facilitating our self-reflective awareness, the former not.

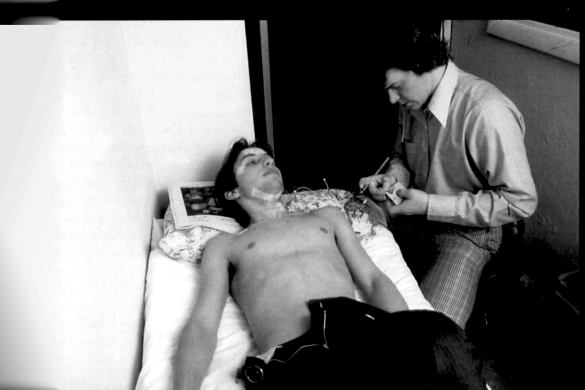

Sleep Lab Hookup.

A technician applies electrodes to the subject's head to record brain waves – the electroencephalogram (EEG), muscle tone with electromyogram (EMG), and the eye movements with the electrooculogram (EOG). This subject was photographed in a hospital sleep lab yielding the images shown on pages 38 and 39.

comitants of fear - rapid heart action, increased blood pressure, and accelerated breathing. We may even struggle to move (to dodge the bayonet) or cry out (for help) and this helps to fracture the dream.

As for the time course of these experiences, Dali is explicit. It all occurs in one second. Each of the six images in the cycle has a duration of about 150 milliseconds, exactly the time interval between successive PGO waves in a well-developed wave cluster. Here Dali has shifted his emphasis on how time is remembered to the phenomenon of time compression in dreams. While it is not true that all dreams occur in the instant before awakening, it is true that those that do are the best remembered. And it is true that such dreams are characterized by time compression. This is the neurobiological basis for what Dali called his "paranoiac-critical method," a spontaneous intuition of irrational knowledge based on the interpretive-critical association of delirious phenomena. At its simplest and most essential, the paranoiac-critical method is the ability of the artist to perceive different images and transformations of images simultaneously within a given configuration.

Freud was wise to reconsider Dali. In 1953, fourteen years after Freud died, the bee in Dali's dream bonnet could begin to be identified as the buzzing of the brainstem neurones which we now take that bee to represent. What we still don't understand is what determines the initial image that initiates the associative chain in dreams; but we choose to remain agnostic on this point, preferring the idea of the role of chance - or randomness - to any suggestion of hidden meaning, be it instinctual, linguistic, or otherwise symbolic representation. Once the sequence is initiated it is not hard for us to see the associative links in the graphically vivid image-emotions that Dali depicts so well.

Sleep Watching: The Invasion of Inner Space

For some must watch while some must sleep,
Thus runs the world away.

William Shakespeare, *Hamlet*

Why did it take so long for scientists to observe sleep directly? Why did science need to wait for the invention of the polygraph, the time-lapse camera, film and video to follow the development of sleep in real time? These questions will be answered more thoroughly in the next chapter but we need to broach them here to understand why moderns, and only moderns, took this task seriously. A general answer as to why they did is that they saw it as an opportunity to understand themselves.

Moderns, and only moderns, were able to break the understandably strong taboo against sleep-watching. The sleeper, having closed the gates of perception and action, is perilously vulnerable. Awakening with someone watching you is distinctly unpleasant. And we all want to sleep in private, especially if we are sleeping with someone else. The reason we do so is because of the close link between sleep and sexuality. There are some good reasons to take this link seriously. One is that the act of sex is both powerfully arousing while it is ongoing and powerfully sedative after its culmination. We do not know whether brain hormone release causes this sedative reaction, but it is easy to see why it might be an adaptive response. What better way to assure fecundation than to guarantee recumbent immobility, muscle relaxation, and hormone release?

We know that hormone release does occur once sleep is initiated. And the hormones that are released include those responsible for growth and for sexual development. Adolescents sleep long and deeply because they are growing and developing sexually. We also know that REM sleep is regularly associated with genital arousal, causing penile erection in males and clitoral engorgement in females. Surprisingly, this has little or nothing to do with dreaming. Erection occurs whether or not the dream content is erotic. It is nonetheless true that young dreamers may have fully climactic sexual release in dreaming sleep.

The private domains of sleep and dreams, including their erotic aspects, are states of virtual reality where anything can happen. Take, for instance, the dream drawing *Le Fort d'Avignon* (1937) from Man Ray's *Les Mains Libres*. A sleeping nude is languorously but precariously stretched out on a bridge resembling the Pont d'Avignon. Her legs are truncated at the knees, suggesting a fragmentary statue of Venus. The vertical column of her strands of hair threatens to pull her off the bridge into the river toward the reflection of her face. Images in the virtual reality of dreams can be ambiguous, appear and disappear, and simultaneously provoke sexual fantasies, apprehension, and anxiety. Is the nude in Man Ray's dream drawing real or a hallucination about to disappear in the depth of the water? Is she alive and sleeping, or an ideally beautiful, inert statue? Is she a colossus, like Gulliver in the land of the Lilliputians, or lying on a miniature bridge?

Consider also Paul Delvaux's *Sleeping Venus* (1945). The title is a citation of a painting by Giorgione of Venus sleeping in a landscape. In contrast to the classically inspired harmony, serenity, and decorum of Giorgione's picture, Delvaux's painting is bizarre, puzzling, and disturbing in the same way that dreams are. A spectral light - Delvaux preferred nocturnal scenes for their association with childhood fears - illuminates a setting with a Greek temple and stoa before a mountainous landscape, and a cast of characters that have no logical relation to each other. The juxtaposition of the sexually available sleeping nude with death in the form of a skeleton and a woman in *fin de siècle* costume is as incongruous as the fact that the erotically charged scenario is staged out of doors in a classical setting.

The painting's perspective construction draws us into its dreamlike realm. But where are we, and what is going on? Speculation as to the symbolism - if there is one - of the picture's content is fruitless. Instead, the picture's meaning, like the meaning of dreams, rests on our subjective response to the formal properties that the work shares with dreams, and to the associations suggested by its images. Marcel Duchamp alluded to this point when he said in a lecture in 1956 that

the creative act is not performed by the artist alone; the spectator brings the work in contact with the external world by deciphering and interpreting its inner qualifications and thus adds his contribution to the creative act.

Among moderns, it was Picasso who first actually looked at sleep in a voyeuristic way and noticed its extreme sensuality and its capacity to enlighten us about our hidden selves. Commenting on Picasso's drawing of a *Youth and Sleeping Girl* the art historian Leo Steinberg has suggested that

Sleep, the interior privacy of the sueño - the state of sleeping and dreaming which in Spanish goes by a single name - may be Picasso's symbol of the innermost self. Once, when challenging the presumption of would-be interpreters of his art, he asked, "How can anyone enter into my dreams?" He was protecting the self in its solitude, but also in its secret inward fertility. The word "dreams" he used as did his Mediterranean ancestors who named the god of dreams Morpheus for the "forms" (morphai) spawned in the imagination in sleep.

Man Ray, *Le fort d'Avignon*, 1937, *Private Collection*.

The virtual reality of Man Ray's dream drawing simultaneously provokes sexual fantasies, apprehension, and anxiety. Is the nude real or a hallucination? Is she alive and sleeping or an ideally beautiful, inert statue? Is she a colossus or lying on a miniature bridge?

The word fertility is used here in its broad autocreative sense, not in the narrowly sexual sense of our current physiological discourse. But the two functions are more than metaphorically associated since both spring from the specific patterns of brain autoactivation in sleep. Remember that the winged god Hypnos was the Greeks' predecessor of Christian angels. He brought dream forms to men while his brothers, Fantasus and Icelus, brought dreams to animals and inanimate objects. Were the pagans completely unrealistic as well as animistic? Do scientists believe that animals dream?

There are, in fact, scientists such as Fred Alan Wolf, author of *The Dreaming Universe*, who believe that the world, even a rock, dreams in the sense that it has a history and memory that can be activated. We take Wolf's point. One can easily imagine that dogs and cats have emotion and percepts in their sleep; but to use the word dreaming without denoting the self-reflective awareness of waking consciousness that allow dreams to be report-

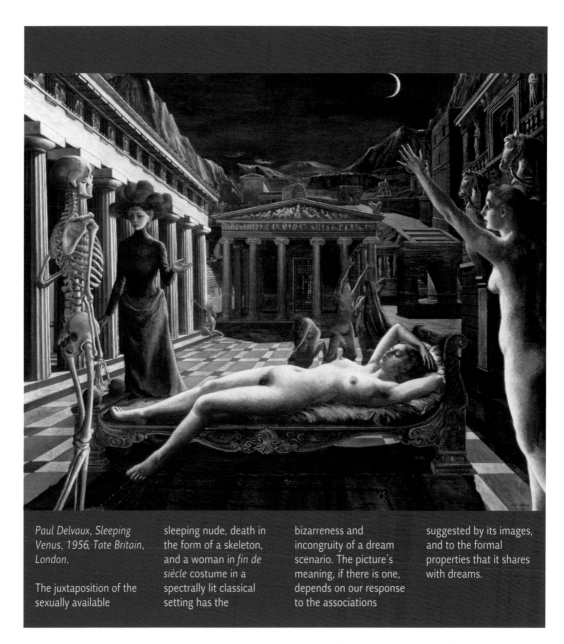

Paul Delvaux, *Sleeping Venus*, 1956, Tate Britain, London.

The juxtaposition of the sexually available sleeping nude, death in the form of a skeleton, and a woman in *fin de siècle* costume in a spectrally lit classical setting has the bizarreness and incongruity of a dream scenario. The picture's meaning, if there is one, depends on our response to the associations suggested by its images, and to the formal properties that it shares with dreams.

ed seems to us to blur an important distinction. We would prefer to use more descriptive terms like activated memory for rocks or activated perceptions and memories for animals. Be that as it may, it is autoactivation that all of theses examples share and that is a universal physical process that needs neither God nor angels to sustain it.

As for the reciprocity of sleep and waking, of watching and being watched in modern art, Steinberg has remarked that

At any moment Picasso's imagery may require one to read his characters not as persons engaged in watching and being watched, but as a figuration of sleeping and waking - dependent states that exclude and presuppose one another, nourish and infect one another, each lacking some richness the other has. In their alternation and reciprocity, we recognize the half-lives our lives are. Hence their inter-changeability in Picasso's art.

We are not sure, however, that watching and being watched can easily be dissociated from being awake and being asleep. The voyeuristic emphasis of Picasso's sleep watchers records the fact that waking consciousness facilitates our self-reflective awareness, while dream consciousness does not. In the early 1930s Picasso explored the relationship between waking and sleeping in a series of erotic paintings of sleeping and dreaming girls with displaced and distorted body parts resembling images that the body can assume in the mind and in dreams - what the perceptual psychologist Paul Schilder called the body-image.

In Picasso's *Girl Before a Mirror* in The Museum of Modern Art in New York, the awake watcher is on the left and the watched sleeper is her own image in the mirror at the right. The waking watcher has two faces, one in sunlight, smiling, and frontal, the other, in profile, moonlit and passive. The watcher extends her arm to hold and caress her mirror image as if in response to the tearful cheek, the inflamed forehead, and the limbus of green that lines that multilayered cowl enfolding the sleeper like a cocoon. The painting celebrates the mirroring function of consciousness. Our consciousness of our bodies and of ourselves is always a construct, as Picasso reveals through the selectiveness and distortions of the double image of the watching and sleeping girl. Self-observation and self-awareness enable us to perceive simultaneously our daytime and nocturnal sides; our alert and withdrawn selves; our waking, sleeping, and dreaming mind states. Through art and science all of these parts are integrated to fulfill and produce models of our creative destinies.

LOOKING AT DREAMS - AND SEEING THEM FOR WHAT THEY ARE

Given the emphasis placed upon the study and depiction of sleep and dreams at the end of the 19th century, we must again emphasize the curious fact that they were not directly observed until the middle of the 20th; and we turn once more to Sigmund Freud, who never conducted the simplest of observational experiments: watching a person sleeping. Had he done so, he might have discovered REM in 1895; and he could have performed awakenings and collected more naturalistic and objective dream data than he did during so many sessions of psychoanalysis.

In fact, any naturalist could have done these things at any time in history. As Michel Jouvet points out in his whimsical fiction-science novel, *Château de Rêve*, REM sleep is directly observable. You don't need an EEG machine to see it. Because the cornea bulges and forms a visible convexity under the closed lids, even the direction of the rapid eye movements can be seen very easily if one only takes the trouble to look. Why then did it take so long for science and art to naturalize dreaming? Why did Freud, Jung, Lacan, and the psychoanalytic community in general not take the trouble to look at dreaming as a generic, natural, and formal cognition process calling for detailed, accurate psychological description that could lead to an explanation that was consonant with biology? That this job of carefully cataloguing dreams, examining their structure, quantifying their distinctive properties, and analyzing those properties in search of a fundamental explanatory hypothesis has only recently been seriously undertaken attests to the ease with which we often bypass straightforward problem solving in favor of perpetuating unverifiable literary and philosophical theories.

In the midst of the philosophical and psychoanalytic theorizing generated in the earlier 20th century, the Surrealists' exploitation of

René Magritte, Pandora's Box, 1951, Yale University Art Gallery. In his neutral, impersonal style Magritte succeeds in creating a dream world with the paradoxical capacity of making incongruous images, such as the mysterious rose, as large as the man's bowler hat, appear compellingly believable, as they do in dreams.

what we have defined as the formal properties of dreams, by de Chirico, Dali, Man Ray, Delvaux and others, found its culmination in the work of the Belgian painter René Magritte. Magritte is the master of the formal analysis of dream consciousness. We will argue that his success as the consummate modern dream painter is in part due to his scientific objectivity and to a genuine desire to emulate dream cognition and emotion rather than use it to illustrate a mystique.

Magritte's paintings have been characterized as photographs of dreams painted by hand. As a consummate example let us take *Pandora's Box*. Upon seeing the deserted bridge, the shadowless light, the anonymous man seen from the back wearing a bowler hat and accompanied by a white rose the size of his head, we automatically say "This is a dream." We submit that the reason for this is that Magritte's painting is a textbook demonstration of our point that art, like dreaming, has the seemingly paradoxical power of making the incongruous appear compellingly believable, and to conjure up the experience of dreaming.

Magritte presents such dreamlike images not as messages to be decoded, but as experiences. His pictures evoke extreme or impossible physical and physiological states or events. David Sylvester has made the point that because they are painted in a neutral, impersonal style, "the spectator is not distracted by speculation as to what is meant [but] is left free to concentrate on what is there." What is there - a locomotive coolly suspended in mid-air in front of a fireplace in place of stove pipe in *Time Transfixed* (1939), or an apple entirely filling an otherwise empty room in *The Listening Chamber* (1953) - can be as strange and unsettling as the disquiet, dread, and panic we experience in dreams. One of the few statements Magritte has made about his intentions is:

Too often by a twist of thought we tend to reduce what is strange to what is familiar. I instead intend to return the familiar to the strange.

Magritte was the first artist to represent incongruity and discontinuity, the essence of dream bizarreness, in a detached, neutral and scientific manner. But because emotion is always part of the story, even when it is only implied, we feel in the presence of his paintings that rather than being instructed about the forms of dreams, we ourselves are in the dream world. Magritte might argue, with modern psychologists like John Antrobus, that waking consciousness is more dreamlike than we recognize.

The locomotive (phallic) and the fireplace (concave, hence vaginal) in *Time Transfixed* would be an easy mark for Freudian psychoanalysts. But that would miss the formal point of the work: the incongruity of objects and settings, which are combined to emphasize the unique particularity of every temporal instant of conscious experience. Magritte himself thought of the painting as a metamporphosis. The locomotive, he laconically said, is

charging out of the chimney opening of the

fireplace in a dining room instead of the usual stovepipe. This metamorphosis is called time transfixed (la durée poignardée).

The representation of time in *Time Transfixed* is a visualization of the experience of time in dreams. Because works of art, like dreams, are closed systems sealed off from inputs from without and not subject to the conditions of how we perceive or judge the world around us, the juxtaposition of the locomotive charging out of the fireplace and a clock that has stopped at 12:44 is as paradoxical as the disorientating in respect to time that we experience in dreams. Like Max Ernst before him, Magritte also pays homage to Giorgio de Chirico. The clock and the locomotive are allusions to the clocks on buildings and locomotives in the backgrounds of paintings by de Chirico of 1913-1914.

By 1939, the year in which Magritte painted *Time Transfixed*, sleep scientists had just begun to attempt all-night sleep recordings and to perceive the ebb and flow of activation and deactivation with a temporal period of 90 minutes. But they did not discover REM because they weren't looking for it. Meanwhile, a major advance in understanding how neurones signaled was being made by Alan Hodgkin and Andrew Fielding Huxley, who discovered that each brain cell could generate its own electrical potential and by suddenly reversing its charge, tell its neighbors to do the same or not to. Freud died in London that year without ever learning about this momentous discovery.

PARADIGM SHIFTS IN SCIENCE

1953, the year in which Magritte painted *The Listening Chamber*, was an annus mirabilis in science. While Magritte was pushing his images of cognitive incongruity to the brink of credulity, Francis Crick and James Watson

René Magritte, The Listening Chamber, 1952, Menil Collection, Huston, Texas.

Magritte raises the question whether the apple is gigantic, or the room is miniature, an ambiguity wich makes the picture as strange and unsettling as the disquiet, dread and panic we experience in dreams.

were unraveling the DNA molecule, and Eugene Aserinsky and Nathaniel Kleitman were discovering REM sleep. Thus the molecular basis of the invisible world of genetics and the functional basis of dreaming were simultaneously brought to light, making possible a science of internal perception, emotion, and memory that is still very much in its infancy and is only beginning to catch up with Magritte, even at the descriptive level.

But can the new science of dreaming tell us what was Magritte was getting at? The best that we can do to answer this question is to describe an experiment whose result suggested that the human mind can see meaning in any juxtaposition, no matter how incongruous it may be. After having discovered, defined, and measured dream incongruity and discontinuity for ourselves - and that only in 1986 - we were still convinced that dreams possessed an overall coherence. We believed they were stories with beginnings, middles, and ends and we believed that this was true even when they were disrupted by scene shifts that changed all formal aspects of narrative, time, place, person, and action.

To test this hypothesis Bob Stickgold cut the typescript reports of such dreams in half with a pair of scissors and then he covertly labeled them Dream I, Part A and Part B, up to twenty dream halves. He then scrambled the A's and B's of the several dreamers and asked our colleagues, some of whom were sophisticated psychoanalysts, to put them back together into the original pairs and in the proper order. The task was impossible. No one, no matter what his expertise, could do any better than chance with these matchings. And yet if these same people saw the dream reports as intact mental products, they were easily convinced of the coherence of the unmatchable dream fragments. One of the things that our experiment suggests is that dream meaning, to paraphrase Marcel Duchamp, is in the eye of the spectator, and, insofar as he is the spectator of his own work, even of the artist.

A case in point is the English painter Victor Willing's account of the genesis of the painting *Place with a Red Thing* in the Tate Britain. From 1978 to 1980 Willing made paintings based directly on hallucinations that correspond in form and character to what the French philosopher Gaston Bachelard called "reveries," states of deep yet conscious imaginings related to but different from dreams that occur in sleep and from daydreams that the mind spins for its own enchantment. Describing his method of working during this period, Willing said that

I would feel very tired but not sleepy, very calm and alert. In this state I would sit down in a comfortable upright chair, relax and stare at the wall. After a time, I could see through the wall – a scene, brightly lit. No figures. No action, just a scene. Objects would appear in three dimensions but as though already drawn in charcoal and pastel. I guess this would last about twenty minutes. I don't think I closed my eyes. I was certainly not asleep – there was never that metabolic change which accompanies sleep, but I would go well into it – so much so that on coming out I would wonder where I was. I would remain in my chair and, taking paper and charcoal, simply copy down the scene. No interpolation was necessary, it had all been done for me – both in the sense of symbol and form. I did not have to do anything. Subsequently meanings might occur to me, but in advance there was nothing. Place with a Red Thing was rather alarming because I think it's a tomb, and to have something growing in a tomb is a rather frightening situation.

Willing's trancelike autocreative state, which, he asserts, was definitely not sleep, is most likely a variant on the theme of meditation, relaxation response, and self-hypnosis, with a dash of hypnagogic hallucination thrown in for good measure. All of these conditions occur at the border between relaxed waking and sleep, and involve an active withdrawal of attention from the outside world. They arise as a function of a slight lowering of brain activation, but also - and more significantly - of an increase in the ratio of internal to external stimulus strength. From our perspective the important point to emphasize is that both in the sense of symbol and form an image emerged spontaneously and automatically from the depth of his artist's brain/mind.

The same autocreative conditions are achieved in dreaming sleep; but they are exaggerated because sleep is accompanied by the "metabolic change" to which Willing refers. As a consequence of the change in the neuromodulatory chemistry of the brain, dream images may be more bizarre, more pleomorphic, and more complex - hence more difficult to copy - than the hallucinatory images that appeared to Willing, and also, because of memory defects, more evanescent. However, the advent of film, as we shall see in chapter 7, made the pictorialization of dreams - and of twilight states like Willing's - seem more easily realizable.

Video Sleeper.

To better document sleep behavior in relation to brain state control, continuous video can be used instead of intermittent time-lapse photographs. We also used video to make visualization of the sleeper's posture and brain state easier for visitors to the *Dreamstage* exhibit. The subject shown here was a young French man recruited to sleep in the Bordeaux wine warehouse where the exhibit (there called *Dreamscreen*) was shown.

Dreaming in Reel Time

Sleep and Dreams in Modern Photography and Film

> *I think that the dream is a lucid thought,*
> *more lucid than any one has when awake,*
> *a thought expressed in images, and at the*
> *same time its form is always dramatic.*
>
> Eugéne Ionesco

Looking at a painting that purports to represent dreaming one can be intrigued, fascinated, and puzzled by its imagery, and at the same time analyze the degree to which the work succeeds or fails to capture essential aspects of the dream process. Throughout this book we have suggested that even painters who were not committed to the representation of dreaming as such have drawn the beholder into an imaginary visual world which is arresting by virtue of its emotional, dreamlike resonance. But paintings, drawings, and prints are static images that must compete for our focused attention with other stimuli from without as well as from within such as our wandering thoughts and fantasies.

We are rarely as single-minded in our contemplation of paintings, including dream paintings, as we are in our dreams. Moreover, dreams are not only more completely enveloping and absorbing than works of art; they are intrinsically more complex because they are not just visual, but involve other sensations, especially the sense of continuous movement. The visual imagery of dreams is dynamic and continually changing, as we are tricked into believing that we are moving through real space and time on extraordinary adventures that we remember and describe as scenarios when we try to recall them as dream reports on awakening.

These characteristics of dreams are shared by films. In this chapter we will discuss the relationship between films and dreams keeping in mind two questions: to what degree is the medium of film intrinsically dreamlike?; and how successfully can it represent dream consciousness? As a prelude to a discussion of the neurobiological correlates between the experiences of dreaming and watching a film, we will consider the general similarities and differences between them. Armed with the emergent model of conscious state determination with which the reader is by now familiar, we will turn to films that shed light on our thesis from three epochs; the early 1920s and

1930s, when modernist artists were first making films about dreams; the 1940s and early 1950s, a time when avant-garde filmmakers, especially in the United States, were experimenting with dreamlike imagery; and finally the period after 1955, when international directors made films combining artistic sensibility and technical sophistication with narrative plots of wide appeal.

Going to the Movies and Dreaming

In the darkness of a movie theatre we are totally enveloped by the imaginary world of the film. Indeed, one of the reasons for the hold that films have over us is that they take over our perceptions and emotions so completely that we can lose our sense of reality, our self-reflective awareness, and our critical stance, and become seamlessly connected to the film's content.

A film can have such a strong hold on us, and we can become so immersed in it that on leaving the theatre after seeing, for example, *Cinema Paradiso*, we are surprised to discover that we are on a street wherever the theatre may be, and not in a village in Italy.

Such geographic disorientation is not unlike the surprise we sometimes experience on waking in a foreign city, having assumed that we were sleeping at home. In the case of films, we may be drawn into the dream world of *Cinema Paradiso*, but we are quickly able to orient ourselves once the film is over. In dreaming, by contrast, our disorientation is complete and continuous. Thus while viewing a film can simulate dreaming, it is not identical with it. As long as the viewer's brain/mind is awake, the competition between the waking state's properties and those of film's artificial simulation of the dream state is biased in favor of waking. The fact that film is so often successful in winning this battle - if only temporarily - is all the more remarkable. It will be useful to keep this dynamic interaction in mind as we proceed.

The New Science of Dreaming and the Making and Viewing of Film

The implications of new data regarding the biological substrata of the dream experience can be extended to a formal consideration of certain parallels between dream generation and cinema. We should, however, not lose sight of the fact that the basic formal differences between the dream state and the waking state that emerge from the new science of dreaming render any artistic treatment of dreaming problematical. Films, like dream reports, are made in the waking state in the medium of language and narrative whose conventions impose severe constraints upon dream simulation. The commitment of film to narration confines it to visual story telling. Dream reports are narrative but dreams are not. Dream films add still another challenge to this problem, which is why so many film makers resort to the stereotyped idiomatic labels of dream films: fuzzy focus, pale shots, soundless vision, flowing gowns, and the like.

These cinematic conventions are successful because insofar as they are indications of the filmmaker's difficulty in representing the dream world, they correspond to the viewer's difficulty in describing his own dreams. Like watching a film, dreaming is a predominantly hallucinatory visual experiences and, like film, is accepted as real. While intense emotion is a common feature of film viewing and dreaming, dreams are more bizarre; scene shifts and transpositions of time, place, events, and persons occur in dreams that waking perception would find difficult to accept, even in a darkened theatre. As a consequence, experimental films that are true to the formal properties of dreaming are so disturbing to watch and so difficult to understand that most film makers

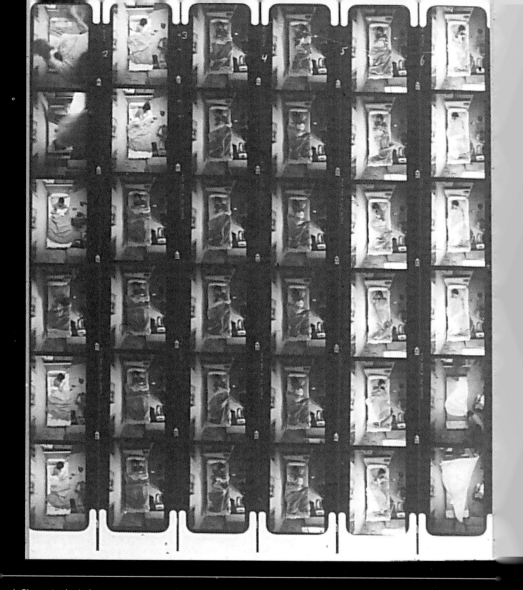

osh Sleeps in the Lab.

As part of a systematic study of the relationship of posture shifts to brain state in sleep we used 400x film, a night light, and a 6 second time exposer to to record the sequential postures and sleep physiology in the lab. This sequence demonstrates the ultimate union of art and science in the study of what Theodore Spagna ca** "hidden landscape".

resort to conventions suggesting the dream experience that are easily understood but transparently unconvincing. Are there alternatives, and what would they involve? We have suggestions for five:

(1) Hallucinatory Aspects. The visual and visuo-motor aspects of dreaming, as we** the curious intensifications and enfe** ments of audition, are easily simulated.

(2) Emotional Aspects. Anxiety, rage elation are easy to simulate in ways induce those feelings in viewers. They are

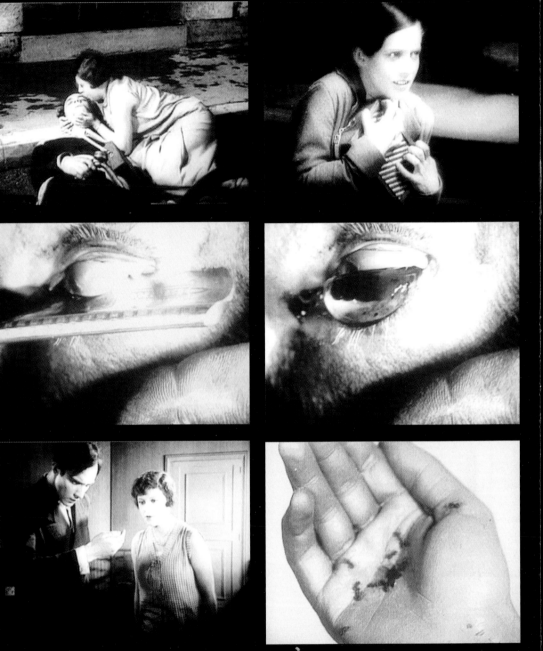

Sequence from Luis Buñuel and Salvador Dali, Un Chien Andalou, 1928.

The sequence from Buñuel and Dali's film captures the essence of dream bizarreness. We applied a scoring system asking the scorer to identify any phrase describing an improbable or impossible item, and to sort it as belonging to plot, thought, or emotion, and to classify it incongruity, discontinuity, and uncertainty or explicit vagueness. See text for explanation.

stuff of effective cinema; and they can be linked to pseudo-hallucinatory imagery in direct and mutually enhancing ways.

(3) Integration of Hallucination and Emotion. We are thinking of films like *The Last Wave* in which the fear-inspiring threat and ambiguity of the visual material is matched with a primordial sound track that intensifies the sense of terror.

(4) Plot Aspects. To bring us to the point of suspending disbelief, films depend on a narrative continuity in which times, places, actions, and persons are portrayed consistently. In dreams this is not at all the case. We seem to be plunged into a maelstrom of sensation and emotion, and buffeted to and fro to an extent that any story, or semblance of a story that we try to construct, is immediately undermined. This is why we define dream bizarreness as orientational instability: times, places, events, and persons change without notice. A number of French filmmakers have experimented with these characteristics of dreaming. The film version of Alain Robbe-Grillet's novel *Last Year at Marienbad* is a relatively successful example.

(5) Memory and Cognition. Film viewers can be tricked into believing almost anything; but they cannot be rendered as quickly and definitively demented as dreamers can. To follow a film we must be able to keep the story line in working memory so as to recognize continuity and congruity even in patently impossible turns in the plot. The suspension of disbelief to which we submit as if temporarily in a hypnotic, trance-like state may, while we are watching a film, reduce critical judgment to a minimum. But we don't inhibit thinking, as we do in dreams. While watching even the most outlandish film, one part of us remains oriented and self-reflective. The fact that we comment on and discuss the film after the lights have come back on shows that the waking brain stayed on course during the dream simulation exercise. This is hardly the case when we awake from a dream. We may try to

remember and talk about the dream, but we do so with a different mind from the one with which we dreamt.

Early Dream Film Experiments

Silent films have been likened to dreams because they distend time and because their silence elicits from the viewer the effort to impute meaning. This occurs occasionally in real dream conversations, when nothing is said but everything is understood. Gary Wills has made the point that in silent films

the sense of time is surreally extended or contrasted, [and] the body is used as an expressive instrument in ways that approach ballet. It is wrong to say these films did not speak. They spoke a different language all their own - visual, aural, emotive. They were interior to the spectator by the very lack of certain kinds of realism. They passed straight into the viewers' dream life.

This appears to have been instinctively understood by the makers of the first silent Surrealist films. Following Freud's arguments in the *Interpretation of Dreams*, André Breton and the Surrealists believed that dreams were a path to the unconscious. Since dreams unfold as sequences of moving images, the visual medium best suited to the exploration of the unconscious without recourse to "good sense and logic," as Giorgio de Chirico put it, is not painting but film. The formal characteristics of film, especially discontinuity and incongruity, were uniquely accessible to the medium of film by means of superimposed images, double exposures, jump cuts, flashbacks, and visions of the future.

The first Surrealist film, *Un Chien Andalou* by Luis Buñuel and Salvador Dali (1928) simulates the dream process through the mechanism of psychic automatism that operates so powerfully in dreams. The images in the film, according to the film historian P. Adams Sitney, were as mysterious to its makers as they are to the spectator. In one sequence in *Un Chien Andalou*, as described by Sitney, a man dressed as a clown, with a striped box held by a thong around his neck, rides his bicycle through city streets. When he falls from it a young woman rushes out of her house, embraces him on the ground, and removes the box around his neck. Back in her room, she lays out articles of clothing and the box as if to reconstruct the man from these mute objects. But suddenly she sees that he is at the other end of the room, now dressed in a suit, staring at the palm of his hand, out of which ants are crawling. In a series of dissolves the ants become a woman's armpit, which in turn becomes a sea urchin and then the top of an androgynous head. The head belongs to a character who stands in the street where the bicyclist had fallen, poking a dismembered hand with a long stick. A crowd gathers around her like ants around the hole in the hand. The police intervene; they push back the crowd; and one of them picks up the hand, places it in the striped box, and gives it to her. As she clutches it to her breast, an automobile runs her down.

While some of the items in this scenario would be unlikely in the content of actual nocturnal dreams, the sequence captures the essence of dream bizarreness in ways to which we can apply our scoring system first published in 1978. The system asks the scorer to identify any phrase describing an improbable or impossible item, to number it, and to sort it as belonging to A (plot), B (thought), or C (emotion); and then to classify it as 1 (discontinuity), 2 (incongruity), or 3 (uncertainty or explicit vagueness). Using this two stage system, the first ten items would be scored as follows:

1. a man dressed as a clown... rides a bicycle A-2 – plot incongruity

2. with a striped box... around his neck A-2– plot incongruity

3. held by a thong A-2 (B-3) – plot incongruity (with ad hoc reasoning)

4. when he falls from it A-2– plot incongruity

5. a young woman embraces him A-2– plot incongruity

6. and removes the box A-2– plot incongruity

7. she lays out articles of clothing A-2 (B-3) – plot incongruity (with ad hoc reasoning)

8. But suddenly she sees [him] dressed in a suit A-1- plot discontinuity

9. staring at the palm of his hand A-2– plot incongruity

10. out of which ants are crawling A-1 (A-2)- plot discontinuity (with incongruity)

As is typical of reports of REM sleep dreams, every line of Sitney's description of this scene contains a distinct instance of bizarreness, as we have formally defined it. By far the most common is plot incongruity (A-2), followed by plot discontinuity (A-1). Explicit descriptions of thinking are absent. The two B-3 items are in brackets because they are only implied; but they are typical of the ad hoc explanations that are common cognitive reactions to bizarre imagery: the box is attached by a thong to explain its already bizarre association with the clown bicyclist; and the woman lays out the box and clothes "as if to reconstruct the man from these mute objects." However logical, this is a weak inference which does not explain the odd behavior of the woman.

A second question arises, which is still beyond the scope of science to answer clearly: is this sequence wholly irrational and aleatory, or does it obey a deeper associational emotional logic? Sitney has suggested that

What Dali and Buñuel achieved through [their] method of compiling a scenario was the liberation of the material from the demands of narrative continuity. Far from being puzzling, the film achieves the clarity of a dream. The concentration on only two actors, male and female, and the insistence on tactile imagery set up a situation of identification [which] in the context of the abrupt dislocations and discontinuities provides us with a vivid metaphor for the dream experience. Had Dali and Buñuel set about to study their own dreams and clinically recreate a dream on film, they could not have surpassed Un Chien Andalou.

Dali's and Buñuel's film is notable not only as a "metaphor for the dream experience." It is also half a century ahead of its time in its protoscientific characterization of dream bizarreness.

THE AVANT-GARDE FILM IN AMERICA

The avant-garde film in the United States during the 1940s and 1950s took the form of the somnambulist, or what Sitney has called trance films, whose prototype was Jean Cocteau's *Le Sang d'un Poéte* (1932). The theme of *Le Sang d'un Poéte* (The Blood of a Poet) is the metamorphosis and personal transformation of the poet as he passes through a series of identifications with his own images. The film uses the plasticity of trance - and to some extent of dreaming - as a vehicle for artistic transformation. Cocteau seems to be saying that the price of artistic commitment is a frightening and potentially self-destructive fluidity of identity that can lead to suicide and death.

The masterpiece of the American genre is *Meshes of the Afternoon* (1943), directed and performed by Maya Deren and Alexander Hammit. Their intention, in Deren's words, was to reproduce

the ways in which the sub-conscious of an individual will develop, interpret and elaborate an apparently simple and casual incident into a critical emotional experience.

Deren and Hammit sought to show how events and objects as they appear during waking become transfigured in dreams, and the way the dreamer may realize that he is dreaming, and may dream that he awakes. Although some of the methods in *Meshes of the Afternoon* derive from *Un Chien Andalou*, its makers did not follow the Surrealist program of evoking a violent, spatially and temporally unstable world without reference to a more conventional reality.

In the film, as Sitney has summarized it, Deren is seated by a window. The camera, shooting through a narrow cylinder, pulls backward, as though drawn into her. Her world lacks all sense of reality; outside, she sees her double. Persons and objects are invested with symbolic meaning: she pursues a black-hooded figure with a mirrored face, seemingly an agent of death. In this oneiric world events unfold in magical fashion: a key is produced from her mouth; a knife tumbles from a loaf of bread; later it reappears on the stairs and in her bed. Logic and causality are torn asunder. Deren turns a phonograph off; but the next time she passes it, the turntable is spinning. One of Deren's doubles lowers a knife to her throat as she sleeps, then seems instantly transformed into a man (Hammit). Later in the couple's bedroom she retaliates, aiming the knife at his face, which is suddenly transformed into a shattered mirror in whose fragments we glimpse the ocean. We are here reminded of paintings by Magritte.

Derealization - seeing oneself in the third person, or even as multiple selves - and symbolization, such as the sexual symbol of the knife, are the hallmarks of dissociative psychopathology. The concept of dissociation was introduced by Pierre Janet in order to

Filming Sleep.

Bed partners' postures tend to mirror each other as shown in this frame from a time lapse study of a couple taken by Edward Schott. This couple is shown in the tender and protective "spoon" position. Sleep is the occasion of intimacy, affection, and bonding which is one reason that is was for so long unobserved. A flash is used to obtain these vivid color images but sleepers adapt well to the invasive light stimuli and the balletic beauty of shared sleep is thus revealed.

deal with the bizarre symptom complexes of hysteria and the puzzling phenomena of hypnotic trance. In essence, dissociation refers to a condition in which the unconscious part of the mind is split off from the conscious part. Psychoanalytic theorists have assumed that derealization is true of dreams as well as of trance. That is not the case. Derealization is surprisingly rare in dreaming, and the sense of the stability of self is surprisingly strong. The tendency in dreaming toward sexual symbolization is largely a Freudian exaggeration.

Keys emerging from mouths, knifes falling from bread, climbing stairs, and entering beds are metaphors rather than dream transformations.

The American filmmaker, Stan Brakhage, was also interested in the concept of film action as a dream world and of the actor as somnabulist. In his film *In Between* (1955) Brakhage is transported from his bed, where he is reading, to an outdoor architectural space filled with classical columns reminiscent of the dreamscapes of Giorgio de Chirico. We wander among the columns as the camera pans wildly, focusing on images of his feet, and inducing in the viewer a sense of vertigo. While the self is almost always the center of perception in dreams, and continuous movement of that self is the rule, the common experiences of unexpected twists and turns of the self's trajectory in dreams normally induce anxiety, but never vertigo. The dreaming brain would seem to be immune to the nauseogenic effects of its own dizzying motor patterns. Put another way, in order to become nauseated the brain needs unpredictably uneven external feedback signals. While Brakhage's films provide such signals, the brain activation of sleep does not.

At this point of our argument we cannot resist introducing *Dreams That Money Can Buy* (1947), a film that is a parody of psychoanalysis and of the psychoanalytically inspired scenarios of commercial dream films, made in New York by the artist and filmmaker Hans Richter in collaboration with Max Ernst, Fernand Leger, Man Ray, Marcel Duchamp, and Alexander Calder. In a series of dream sequences it tells the story of Joe, a young poet desperate for recognition, who opens an office in which he sells his clients dreams based on material he elicits from their unconscious.

To his first client, a bank clerk who doesn't make enough money and is a poor lover, Joe sells a voluptuous dream of a sleeping girl whose unconscious engages in an enraptured soliloquy. Shipwrecked bodies are dragged from under her bed, and her bedroom floats through a jungle of threatening corridors and dungeons. When her lover finally joins her, the girl's solitary dream is superseded by exuberant visions symbolizing the ecstasy of love and its vibrant afterglow.

Another of Joe's clients is the bank clerk's wife in search of her lost youth. Joe sells her a dream that is set in a movie theatre, where the woman loses herself in the illusion of identifying with her screen idols and disappears. The last dream is Joe's own. Joe is climbing a ladder, intent on following his destiny, but one rung after another vanishes under his feet. As the dream salesman discovers his own identity, his face turns blue. A bust of Zeus, a symbol of Joe's dearest memories, shatters to bits, and Joe as a person dissolves.

THE INTERNATIONAL ART FILM

Beginning in the early 1950s and extending to the mid-1970s the treatment of dreams by Ingmar Bergman and Federico Fellini was heavily influenced by Freudian and Jungian psychoanalytic dream theories. Ironically, it was Bergman, the refugee from the sternness of Scandinavian Protestantism, who embraced Sigmund Freud, while Fellini, the renegade Italian catholic, was fascinated by Carl Jung. In our necessarily brief and selective discussion of this period in Bergman's and Fellini's work, which corresponds precisely to the first phase (1953-1975) of modern sleep and dream science, we will attempt to show how each of these filmmakers dealt with questions raised by the neurophysiological study of dreams. Our general conclusion will be that both represented dreams as transparently clear messages about personal conflict and personal transformation. Despite their indebtedness to psychoanalytic theory and

Bergman's Wild Strawberries. Opening Dream Sequence. Isak Berg coming face to face with his own death. (For a detailed analysis see text).

their acknowledgment of dream symbolism, both saw dreams as the mind's effort to reveal rather than to conceal, to instruct rather than to befuddle.

The Dream Films of Ingmar Bergman

To illustrate the shift of the model for the dream film from psychoanalysis to activation synthesis, it is helpful to compare the relatively literary treatment of dreams in Bergman's early masterpiece *Wild Strawberries* (1957) with his more formal analysis of borderline mental states in his later film, *Persona* (1966). The coffin dream of *Wild Strawberries*, has many direct references to Freudian theory. In his choice of images, Bergman draws on Surrealism and Expressionism, two artistic derivatives of psychoanalysis. He then organizes them within the narrative dream of the story. The film is a clinical tour-de-force in its representation of the relationship between life history, personal crisis, and dream symbolism. But the film's borrowings from literary and psychological sources fail to convey key formal aspects of dream phenomenology.

Some of these formal aspects do appear in the opening montage sequence of *Persona*. While certain images in this sequence are associated with each other as dictated by psychoanalytic theory, the imagery in general is not nearly as psychoanalytically pregnant. Rather, Bergman's choice of images and their organization as a tachistoscopic montage suggest the emergence of a concern for the formal logic of vision and cinematography. The story line is abandoned, and the brutal narrative shifts achieved by cutting seem designed to define and test the limits of the viewer's visual perception.

Whether or not Bergman intended this sequence to represent a dream, its experimental approach to perception justifies linking it with aspects of the neurophysiology of the dream process that we have discussed in chapter 2. In this sense it is formally related to Stan Brakhage's *In Between*, the difference between the two being that while Bergman represents vertigo even more clearly than Brakhage, he does not induce it as such in the viewer.

The "Coffin" and the "Examination" Dreams of *Wild Strawberries*

Wild Strawberries is a film about Isak Borg, an aging physician-turned-scientist, who goes back to his alma mater, Lund University, to receive an honorary degree. On the way he stops to visit the summer house of his childhood. Its wild strawberry patch triggers a flood of memories. Borg sees himself as hesitant and moralistic, character traits that have shaped and limited his life. As the trip continues, Borg's daughter-in-law, who accompanies him, accuses him of coldness; and these accusations are amplified by the vicious argument of a middle-aged couple and the teasing of a young trio whom Borg and his daughter-in-law pick up.

In Lund, a chilling confrontation with his mother traces Borg's life problem to its root source. At the end of the film, he drifts off to sleep. His stern temperament has been softened by his honorary degree, the faint hope that his daughter-in-law will give him a grandchild, and the tender farewell of the young trio.

The coffin dream occurs on the eve of Borg's departure for Lund and foreshadows his death. To signal the dream state, Bergman employs a dissolve from the face of Borg asleep to his face in the dream. The dream's dramatic content consists of three segments in an emblematic narrative style using a series of Surrealist devices and symbols.

In the first segment Borg is walking on a

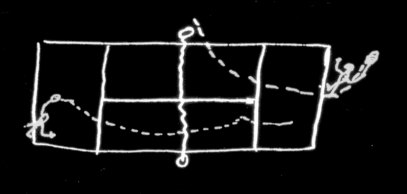

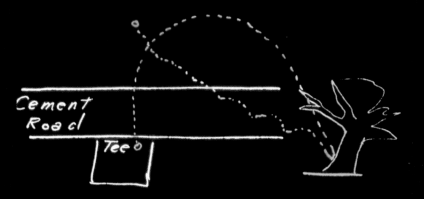

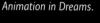

Animation in Dreams.

These drawings, from the dream journal of a Smithsonian insect specialist, show the unusual trajectories taken by dream tennis serves, dream golf balls and dream base runners. Dreamers zig and zag not because they are being pulled around dream space by external agents but because the motor systems of their brain are being activated in sleep. By coloring more and more of the dashed lines indicating movement in the drawings, it is possible to create an animated sequence showing these bizarre trajectories. Dream movement is as incongruous as other elements of dream plots. Our brain's capacity to simulate veridical movement is thus altered in sleep. It has been suggested that the brain is running all its motor programs in a helter-shelter way so that modifications based upon recent experience can be made during sleep. This is what is called procedural learning.

deserted street; there is an intense, whitish light, and the windows of the houses he is passing are boarded up. The scene suggests isolation, darkness, and blindness and has the dreamlike atmosphere of paintings by Giorgio de Chirico. Borg walks under the sign of an optometrist's shop that is actually a clock and a pair of spectacles. The face of the clock has numbers on it but it has no hands, an allusion to death. Borg walks under the sign and turns to look at its other side, which has numbers but again no hands. The pair of spectacles has painted eyes, one of which appears to be cut and bleeding - a direct reference to the slashing of an eye in the opening sequence of *Un Chien Andalou*. Borg then takes out his own watch, as if to check his growing suspicion that time has run out, and notices that it, too, has no hands. On the soundtrack a heart beats and then stops. The first dream sequence ends as the confused Borg paces nervously up and down under the sign.

The second segment begins as Borg sees a man in a dark coat standing on the previously empty sidewalk. He approaches the man from behind and taps him on the shoulder. As the man turns we see horror on Borg's face before noticing that the stranger's eyes, like the windows of the boarded-up house, are shut. His face has a fetal, physically deformed expression. After a sudden cut the man falls. Blood is flowing from his neck, but his head cannot be seen. A death knell sounds as a clock begins to strike.

At the beginning of the third segment Borg sees at a distance an approaching funeral cortege. The horse-drawn carriage hits a lamppost and the lamp breaks. A wheel of the carriage comes loose and rolls toward Borg, then crashes against the wall of the house and breaks. The carriage slips on its axis and begins to creak with a sound suggesting at the same time a baby's cry and the last gasp of a dying man. The evocation of birth and death

is underscored by a shot of a cherub on the top of the hearse. As the creaking sound continues a coffin slides out of the hearse and its lid opens. A hand appears on the coffin's edge. We assume, before we see it, that the face in the coffin will be Borg's. Borg grasps the hand and is pulled toward the coffin. The camera pans back and forth from Borg's face within and outside the coffin: he is face-to-face with his own death. His coffin face then dissolves to his face in bed, ending the dream as it began. Borg lies still, gets up disoriented, opens the shades, and notices it is daylight. He looks down at his own clock and he establishes contact with the world of waking.

This film sequence is pregnant with a sense of dread and foreboding achieved by the mounting harbingers of death. The images are intrinsically bizarre in their incongruity, and they are linked in discontinuous sequences whose logic depends, as it does in dreams, on the congruence of each image to a dominant theme of anxiety. From a formalistic point of view, the sequence, which lasts five minutes, is composed of three clearly distinct segments lasting between one and two minutes, each with its own intense emotionality and hallucinatory activity. This crescendo-decrescendo pattern and its periodicity correspond perfectly to the periodic rise and fall of internal activation of the brain's perceptual-emotional and autonomic centers during REM sleep.

The second dream in *Wild Strawberries* occurs as Borg dozes in the automobile en route to Lund. It is strikingly different from the first in that it is entirely narrative and employs far fewer symbols. In the first of its six clearly defined segments we see Borg's lost love, Sara, in the wild strawberry patch. She holds a mirror up to Borg, asking him to see himself as an old man who is going to die. She mocks his intellectual sophistication and his lack of insight into life, and is pleased that these remarks hurt him. In the second segment Sara leaves Borg and runs to comfort

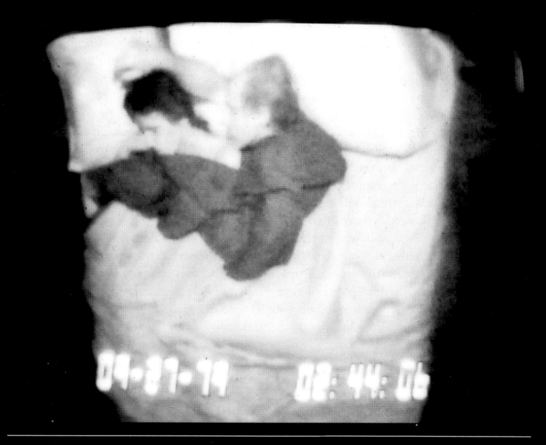

Joan and Allan sleep on TV.

Using commercial time lapse video, it is possible to document the natural sleep of bed partners and to show that the posture shifts that demarcate the NREM-REM sleep cycle are synchronized throughout the night. In small beds, like this one, every posture shift by one partner triggers a posture shift in the partner.

and coddle her baby. Borg is seeing something that he has never experienced. Sara then runs to the house and goes in. In the third segment Borg watches through a window as Sara and her husband kiss at the piano before sitting down for a meal at a richly laid table. Borg is again an outsider seeing what he has never experienced - domestic happiness. The fourth segment begins as Borg goes from Sara's house to another building. He knocks on the door. Placing his hand on the door jamb, he runs it onto a nail. The image of the bleeding hand suggests the stigmata. There is the sound of a beating heart, reminding us of the first dream sequence, and of Borg's impending death.

In the fifth segment the door opens and Borg is led down a hallway to an examination room. The examiner is Borg's sadistic son, the husband of Borg's daughter-in-law who drove them to Lund. The jury in the examination room sits in rows of seats resembling pews or a medical amphitheatre. Borg is first asked to identify a specimen. Looking through the microscope, he sees his own eyes - a visual echo of the eyes painted in the lenses of the spectacles on the sign of the optometrist's shop in first dream. The examiner asks Borg to define a doctor's first duty. When Borg cannot answer, the examiner tells him that it is to "ask forgiveness." Later Borg is asked to diagnose a patient.

He says she is dead; but she laughs, mocking his inability to distinguish life from death. The examiner has reached a verdict: Borg is incompetent and guilty of callousness, selfishness, and uselessness. These accusations, the examiner tells Borg, were made by his wife, who in the sixth segment of the dream re-enacts a rape which Borg had witnessed thirty years earlier, but to which he cannot respond. When his wife asks for his forgiveness he answers that there is nothing to forgive. Borg's punishment for his offenses is loneliness. "Is there no mercy?" Borg asks. "No mercy," the examiner replies.

The dream is loaded with specific historical material only slightly transposed to suggest the dream state. The meaning of the dream is neither concealed nor disguised. Rather it is transparently clear: Borg has forfeited the fullness of life by turning away from the direct and simple needs of humanity to the abstract, elusive goals of science. He looks back on his life, as the coffin dream looks forward to his death. Together the two dreams bracket the film's message that a life of coldness ends in sadness and isolation. A third dream in the film underlines this conclusion: there are no wild strawberries left.

Bergman's use of the dream idiom to tell a compelling biographical story is subtly different in the two dreams. In the examination dream it is more direct and unconcealed than in the coffin dream. In both, however, the plot is more unified and sustained than would be expected in natural dreaming, where microscopic bizarreness normally renders the dream action more chaotic, and macroscopic scene changes may derail an emerging scenario and substitute a second one that cannot be related to the first. Actual dream reports of the length of the two dream sequences would contain between ten and a hundred times more micro-bizarreness; the emotional tone would be far more variable, and two or three major scene changes would be expected. The point we wish to emphasize here is that even at their most bizarre and symbolic, Borg's dreams are transparent and undisguised. Their meaning is crystal clear.

The Montage Sequence of *Persona* and the Representation of Vertigo

It is known that *Persona* was conceived when Bergman was in a hospital suffering from vertigo. Vertigo is experienced when an infection or other abnormality in the inner ear sends a message to the central nervous system saying that the head is moving. But the vertigo patient's head is not moving, and he therefore experiences space as moving around him as in dreaming sleep. These signals generate eye movement, since every real or simulated movement of the head requires compensatory eye movements to stabilize perceptual space. This triggers a sequence of unusual visual images. We speculate that to avoid the nauseous consequences of vertigo, Bergman closed his eyes and saw the sort of sequence he designed for the opening scenes of *Persona*. Closing one's eyes has three related consequences: elimination of the incompatibility of internal and external visual information about body position, relief of nausea, and the predominance in perception of internal sources of information.

The film opens with two vague light spots which, as they slowly come into focus, are revealed as the two points of a carbon lamp that illuminate the film projector. Bergman seems to be saying that light is the source for the energy that drives both the film projector and visual perception. From the perspective of psychophysiology the opening of the film suggests the internal generation of light during the dream when the outside world is dark. Sight has to be generated within the nervous system; and the brain is both the projector and the screen of dream imagery. During waking the brain acts like a camera that incorporates

Bergman's Persona.

Ingmar Bergman's
Persona has an opening

sequence of incongruous
but emotionally salient
images. After tracing the
development of his

interest in film he then
turns to menacing images
such as these. The
autobiographic signature

is in the lower right frame.

images into memory and analyzes them on-line for perceptual content. During the dream state the visual system of the brain acts like a projector or image generator, pulling stored images out of memory and assembling them into a synthetic perceptual whole. The visual product of this internal process may be quite different from anything actually seen during waking.

In the next scene of the film Bergman turns to specific references to his personal history and psychology in relation to film. An inverted cartoon image recalls his childhood cine-matography, technical naiveté, and arbitrary image distortions. A subsequent sequence of dreamer, robber, and policeman integrates the animation technique into a sleep-dream story. Psychophysiologically, the development from crude to symbolic imagery resembles the dif-ference between the perceptual and ideational levels of visual experience. The following sequence - a series of primordial images inter-spersed with jump cuts - produces a sense of strikingly dreamlike scene shifting.

Not all dreams are integrated by story lines, as we are led to believe by the stories we tell when we report them. Radical and unpre-dictable shifts of scene may occur instead. A

The Nightcap.

To be able to record sleep at home we have invented a teo channel event-recorder called the Nightcap, which can deduce the state of the brain from movements of the head and the eyes. Head movements are recorded by placing an accelerometer in the head band and eye movements are recorded from a piezofilm applied to the left upper eyelid. When there is activation in both channels the algorithm scores wake, when there is none NREM sleep. REM is scored when eye movement is high and head movement is low. Using this device we can study sleep and dreaming in its natural setting and obtain much more data for much less money.

sequence of scenes in a dream may be integrated by a particular emotion such as fear or dread, or by a thematic image, such as penetration. Throughout the cuts in the *Persona* sequence, from a spider/to a sheep/to a spike driven through a hand/to trees in snow/to a spiked fence surmounting piles of snow, the associative chain is clear; only the fragmentation requires explanation.

In the light of our activation-synthesis hypothesis, fragmentation is a feature of the generator process in the brain, and the scene cuts and shifts are its inevitable result. The transformations from cut to cut do not disguise or neutralize the sequence's emotional impact. The sense of fear and dread continues across the scene changes, and is even intensified by the incisive renewal of attention that they command. As in this sequence in *Persona*, dreams are generally less a story than a sequence of visual images linked by strong emotion. Bergman announces the end of the prologue and the beginning of the film proper by mixing the numbers of the film leader with his titles and a series of tachistoscopic images. He is now using the technical properties inherent in film and the technical capacities of the editing process to simulate the image-generating capacities of the brain. For this reason *Persona* is a more accurate representation of formal properties of dreaming than the more explicit rendering of dreams in *Wild Strawberries*. We have come a long way from Dali and Buñuel's *Un Chien Andalou*. While Bergman recognizes and incorporates the bizarre qualities of dreams, he uses them to enhance rather than to negate narrative flow.

The Dream Films of Federico Fellini

Federico Fellini takes the approach a step further, as he devises a theory of creativity that is closely tied to his vision of dreaming. Fellini's dream theory, inspired by Jungian ideas of dream transparency and artistic inspiration, is as different from Bergman's adherence to Freud as activation synthesis is from classical psychoanalysis. For Freud the apparent disorder of dreams represented a transformation of impulsive truth into phenomenological chaos. For Fellini, as for activation synthesis, the phenomenological chaos of dreams is a primary rather than a secondary event; the brain-mind is seen as intrinsically chaotic, random, and unpredictable; and the imaginative aspects of dreaming - and of film - arise from the chaotic agitation of the brain's sensorimotor, emotional, and mnemonic centers.

In his account of the creative process in an interview with Dick Cavett, Fellini clearly described the basic principles of the activation-synthesis hypothesis of dreaming. Dick Cavett asked him:

Is it possible, Mr. Fellini, to explain where the idea for a movie came from? I often wonder about someone like yourself, when you're walking around Rome or New York, do you suddenly think, "Aha! There's something I want to make into a film?" Or, is it sort of bubbling and simmering inside?

Here is part of Fellini's reply:

It should be more nice like that, walking in New York -
"Aha!" It is very difficult to try to reach when the first original idea comes into your mind. I think it's a mix of vocation, destiny, and professional attitude to concentrate, to live like a guest in life, to be like a tourist. The idea for a picture can come in such many different ways. First of all, you have to have souvenirs (memories), you have to have temperament, you have to have direction, you have to hate and to love, you have to be a human machine. Sometimes a picture comes from a little fragment of a souvenir, a little piece of music or a smell. I don't want to appear romantic, but a picture comes to you in a thousand little pieces. You feel that a little piece has to do with something

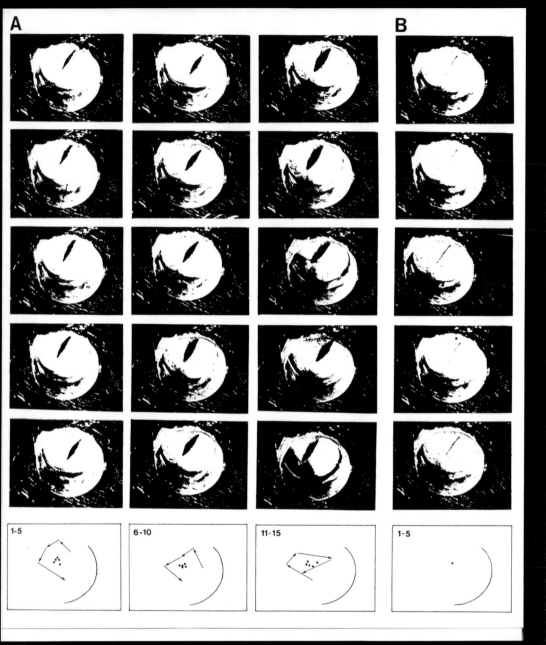

Cat Eye Movement in Sleep.

When he was still working on sleep in Giuseppe Moruzzi's Institute of Physiology in Pisa, Giovanni Berlucchi made a movie of the cat's eye in REM sleep. By implanting a stainless steel cylinder, Berlucchi was able to show that the immobile eye with its pupil completely closed in NREM sleep (column B) began to wiggle and gyrate in REM (column A).

By looking at the analysis of the movements below it can be seen that the eye moves continuously and that the largest jumps (frames 9-15) are associated with dramatic widenings of the pupil. During REM sleep dreaming, it is actually difficult to introduce external stimuli because the brain is so busy processing its own information.

more complete, so you start to collect, you start to find things around. At a certain moment you have the impression that something is near you, some shape or some phantom, let's see, in a more psychological way. And you know that this creature in your imagination wants something from you, it wants to be incarnato. Now starts the real problem: to find the money to permit the phantom to be materialized. And the phantom does not help you at all, he wants only to be materialized. You got to find some other people.

Let us consider this statement in terms of activation synthesis: First there are the building blocks that are the memories of experience, the "thousand little pieces" that are encoded in our sensorimotor neuronal circuits. Then there are the emotional associations, including memories of experiences of love and hate, emanating from the emotional wellspring that Fellini calls temperament. These are the emotional states that are activated when limbic lobe structures are turned on in dreaming sleep, often automatically, and sometimes secondarily, but always in association with sensorimotor factors.

There is, finally, the synthesis of the sensorimotor and emotional factors that emerge as shapes and phantoms which demand incarnation by the imagination. This synthetic process takes place automatically via the connections between the sensorimotor and emotion circuits of the brain that are integrated in the frontal cortex. While the automatic synthesis is being performed in dreaming sleep the frontal cortex is enfeebled; but it can use the products of the synthesis if and when the brain-mind rouses itself from waking fantasy or from dreaming sleep. To illustrate this process let us look at some scenes from Fellini's artistic autobiography, the film called *8 1/2*.

The story line of *8 1/2* is clear and straightforward. Guido, a filmmaker, is in a creative and personal crisis. He doubts his capacity to unify the fragmentary ideas inspiring his film-in-progress. His self-doubt is expressed and amplified by the recurrent commentary on his ideas by the critic Daumier, by the financial anxiety of his producer Canocchio, and by the moral censure of the cardinal. Guido's distraction from his work is aggravated by his obsessive promiscuity. His mistress Carla, the bevy of film bimbos who pursue him relentlessly, and Claudia, whom he would like to seduce, all help to keep him excited, but render him anxious and dysfunctional. When his wife Luisa arrives at the spa where he has gone for a cure, it becomes clear that his marriage of twenty years hangs by a thread. In the climactic scene he responds to the accusation that he has nothing to say and doesn't know how to love by admitting his artistic and personal confusion, acknowledging his creative and amorous polymorphism, and asking Luisa to accept him as he is. Luisa questions his rectitude but agrees to his proposal. He is then able to complete his film.

Although the story evolves sequentially, it is fractured by scenes representing Guido's mental state, including his dreams, his fantasies, and his ruminations. It is not always easy to tell which of these three different psychological processes Fellini intends to represent. What matters is Fellini's attention to the constant oscillation between foreground plot structure and background mental processes that interact so dynamically, so associatively, and so seamlessly with the foreground plot as to make even the distinction between foreground and background levels of experience - and their analysis - seem artificial. Fellini is saying that what is going on in the outside world is no more real - or significant - than what goes on inside one's head. It is the way Fellini represents the phenomenology of subjective experience that is of particular interest to us.

By our reckoning there are thirty-six scenes in *8 1/2*, of which eighteen can be attributed to the foreground plot, and eighteen to a variety of background mental processes. Only two

basis of our capacity to visualize, to imagine, and to create derives from the autogenic character of the brain as image maker, and from out ability to tap and even to control image generation in our own heads. Fellini's acceptance of the internal world as real and as true helps us suspend belief and accept the delusional aspect of the scenes we have identified and their imputed meaning. Indeed, for Fellini the internal world is a more important source of truth than the world around us with its constraints and demands that threaten to block impulses surging from within.

We know that in REM sleep image generation is impelled by surges of information and energy automatically arising from the brain stem centers that command and coordinate eye movement. These signals stimulate the visual brain as if they were codes reporting on light from the external world. The origin of this internal source of data is the motor centers of the brain stem; and this may account for the dramatic movements in dreams, like the flying sequence which opens *8 1/2*. Such movement is, of course, fictive, because it doesn't happen in a muscular sense; but it is no less real for all that, for it is commanded and experienced by the dreaming brain as realistically as it would be in waking.

The visual brain is not the only target of these surges of endogenous stimulation. They also invade the emotional brain via a pathway from the brain stem to the amygdala in the temporal lobe, where they set off storms of intense feeling that constitute and shape dream consciousness. Fellini seems to know this intuitively. Thus in the opening scene of *8 1/2* Guido is stricken with panic as he struggles to escape from the car, flies away and is pulled back to earth by a rope (perhaps meant to represent his social obligations), and, as the scene ends, he falls into the void with classic nightmare vertigo. Similarly, anxiety permeates

Swedenborg's Angels.

When the Swedish biologist, Emmanuel Swedenborg, failed to behold god through his microscope, he turned to dream incubation and succeeded. By depriving himself of sleep, he caused REM pressure to increase until he was flooded with visions of angels who instructed him to create the Church of New Jerusalem. Swedenborg is at the transition point from the animistic to the physicalistic models of human consciousness. His self-observations clearly reveal that dreaming can be manipulated and that dreams can be made to contain whatever the dreamer is looking for.

scenes appear intended to represent dreams. Of the other mental process scenes, two can be classified as memories, and two as fantasies. It is from these six scenes that we will draw material for our discussion.

From the formal point of view, Fellini represents the internal world of dream, fantasy, and reflection as a visual hallucinoid process. This constant feature of even voluntary image

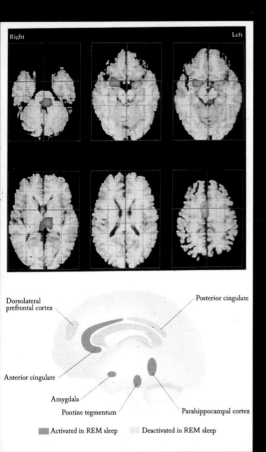

Right | Left

Dorsolateral
prefrontal cortex

Posterior cingulate

Anterior cingulate

Amygdala

Pontine tegmentum

Parahippocampal cortex

■ Activated in REM sleep   ■ Deactivated in REM sleep

Pet Images of the Human Brain in REM Sleep.

By injecting radioisotopes during waking or sleep, it is possible to estimate regional neuronal activity as shown here for REM sleep compared to waking. Among the structures color coded to indicate higher activation than in waking are the pontine brain stem (which is thought to generate REM), the limbic system (which is thought to generate emotions), and other parts of the upper brain (which may integrate emotions with cognition). It is significant that structures which are not

as active as they are in waking include the dorsolateral prefrontal cortex (thought to be responsible for executive cognitive functions like directed thought). These structures probably mediate the emotionally salient cognitions of dreams and the lack of control and critical recognition that characterizes dreaming. The images were kindly provided by Pierre Maquet.

Guido's anticipations of his encounter with the cardinal and with the unhappy women in his life.

The experience of existential and circumstantial anxiety in Fellini's own life played an important part in his creative style. Instead of regarding anxiety as a symptom, Fellini accepted - indeed, celebrated - his own anxiety. With its attendant excitement and confusion, anxiety fuelled Fellini's creative adventurousness. After anxiety, the most prevalent dream emotion is elation (in waking the order is the other way around). Both the experience and the representation of elation were among Fellini's greatest gifts. His childlike, seductive, comic playfulness kept his actors, his hangers-on, his women, and his guests all intrigued no matter how irritated they might occasionally become.

In the opening dream of *8 1/2* Guido flies as his mother puts him to bed, laughs as Saraghina does the rhumba, and dances. In the closing scene he plays the pipe in a circus band. And in his appeal to Luisa he says: "Life is a holiday, let's enjoy it together." In doing so he accepts reality, including his own deeply personal reality, confused as it may be, even to the point of defying any single interpretation or explanation. He accepts himself as he is, not as he would like to be. He then tells Luisa that he is no longer afraid to tell the truth, that he dares to seek even if he cannot find. Only in this way can he look into her faithful eyes without shame. Declaring that life is a holiday, he invites her to enjoy it with him. She expresses skepticism whether he is right or not. But she agrees, with his help, to try to accept him. Guido picks up his megaphone and begins to direct his film.

SUMMARY AND CONCLUSIONS

Modern film makers and dream scientists share many basic assumptions and methodologies. Both are skeptical of received ideas, and both are motivated to find new ways of perceiving, understanding, and explaining nature, including human nature. In relating Fellini's artistic dream vision to modern dream science we have been able to discern striking parallels at the levels of form, style, and content. Many facts, many little pieces of information are the essential ingredients of the creative act, which itself is a virtually automatic synthesis of data until an idea, phantom, or shape emerges. In respect to the content of this process, both Fellini and neurophysiology share a recognition of the deep reciprocity between chaos, be it neuronal or social, and self-organization, be it the scientific idea, the dream image, or the film.

In bringing this chapter to an end we would like to reiterate that the new vision which emerges from both Fellini's films and modern dream science is radically different from the deterministic model of Newtonian science that informed Freud's view of the unconscious. In its emphasis on chaos and self-organization in the emergence of normal mental structures, the new vision assigns a formative role to chance and to a process leading to unpredictable results. The mind, for Fellini and for the neurophysiologist, is both free to be determined, and determined to be free.

LES RÊVES

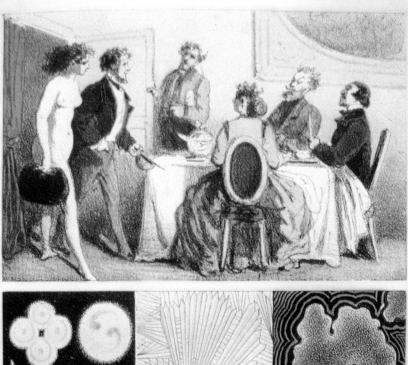

Hervey de Saint-Denis, Frontispiece of Les Rêves et Les Moyens de les Diriger, 1867.

In the frontispiece of his book Hervey depicted two kinds of visual imagery at different stages of sleep: the fully formed, realistic dream scenario, and the geometric, kaleidoscopic phantasms at sleep onset. He ascribed the latter to retinal stimuli, the former to dreams' access to memories. Neither he nor any of his contemporaries imagined that the brain itself might be the source of dream stimulation.

The Art of Dreaming

Creativity and the Dream State

> *Be cheerful, Sir.*
> *Our revels are now ended. These are actors,*
> *As I foretold you, are all spirits and*
> *Are melted into air, into thin air...*
> *...We are such stuff*
> *As dreams are made on, and our little life*
> *Is rounded with a sleep.*
>
> William Shakespeare, *The Tempest*

In general it is fair to say that the waking brain is better at linear logic, at analysis, at quantification, and at critical judgment than the dreaming brain. Conversely, the dreaming brain is better at analogical thinking, comparing apparently unrelated associations, at visualization, at the expression of emotion, and at creating virtual reality of remarkable integrity given the fact that it has only its own resources to do so.

At first glance, it might seem that the waking brain would be more naturally gifted for science and the dreaming brain for art, but that formulation is both oversimplified and erroneous. Oversimplified because both art and science need the optimal qualities of both waking and dreaming states, and erroneous because both art and science can only be pursued - or finally enacted - in the waking state. It will be the main goal of this chapter to explore those aspects of dreaming sleep which epitomize the creative capacities of the brain and then to show how these capacities can be accessed and enhanced during the waking state. Whether we are engaged in creating art and science, or simply trying better to understand and appreciate our creative potential, dream science has much to tell us.

DETERMINISM AND UNPREDICTABILITY IN ART-SCIENCE MODEL BUILDING

The 20th century witnessed a paradigm shift from Newtonian physics with its assumption of strict determinism to the indeterminacy of quantum physics, and to the concepts of greatest interest to us in this chapter, chaos and self-organization. It is important to summarize the developments of dream science over the last one hundred years in terms of this particular paradigm shift.

Freud's theory of dreams was based upon the concepts of psychic determinism derived from Newtonian physics. Because Freud's model of the brain had no capacity for spon-

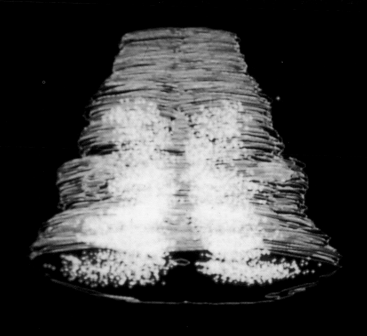

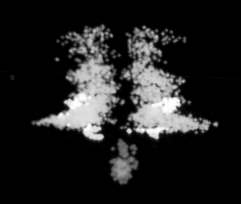

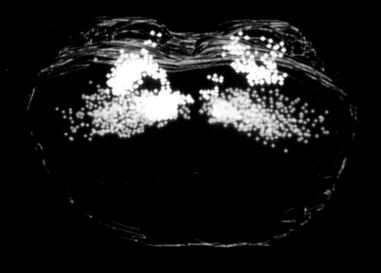

Visualization and Modelling in Science.

When scientists want to represent and communicate their concepts visually they may resort to abstract images like those created by James Quatrocchi. By microinjecting a molucule that induces REM sleep and is transported back to the cells projecting to the induction site we were able to produce these computerized maps of the REM generation network in the cat brain stem. The neuronal network includes the pontine reticular formation (blue) the raphe nucleus (red) the locus coeruleus (yellow) and the peribrachial nuclei (orange and white). These findings combined with neuronal recording data give a more complete picture of how the brain may change its state from waking to dreaming.

taneity, randomness, chaos, and self-organization, and no capacity for novelty, autocreativity, and inventiveness, psychoanalytic dream theory emphasizes a constant conflict between instinctual drives and psychic equilibrium. In Freud's view, art and dreams, in order to be genuinely understood, were to be approached as symptoms in need of psychoanalytic interpretation.

Subsequent neurobiological studies revealed that many of Freud's assumptions about the brain were erroneous. At the same time that physicists were radically modifying Newton's ideas, neurobiologists were discovering that the human brain exemplified many of the new principles that characterized other complex physical systems. Not only was the brain capable of spontaneous action (and thus was the originator rather than simply a duplicator of it own drives), but the brain was constantly reworking its memory system, actively discarding obsolete material, and restlessly seeking new ways of seeing, being, and feeling.

Recent revisionist commentators on Freud have not always taken into account the argument of Lesley Chamberlain, the author of *The Secret Artist: A Close Reading of Sigmund Freud* (2003), that there are at least two Freuds, a French, literary Freud, and an Anglo-Saxon, scientific Freud. Chamberlain has made the point that in *The Interpretation of Dreams*

Freud attributes to the unconscious the power of a writer brilliantly deploying the classical tropes to transform his material. For many of us, fascinated by the interplay which infected the Joyce of Finnegan's Wake and by the interface of philosophy and metaphor, Freud tried to catalogue the mind's inventiveness against a backdrop of modern philosophy. There is something of Locke and Hume, but also of Brentano's phenomenology, in his account of how we represent the world to ourselves, how our mental representations link up with words, how objects come to be thought about by association with each other, and what it is for an object to exist only in the mind. This eclectic philosophical mixture underlies his account of the unconscious. The Dreambook, with its wonderful exploration of language, is the key to the French Freud. Lacan rightly brings out the strong affinity between Freud's sense of drama and his work on dreams. That is another reason why we continue to read... his great book on the creative process. Anglo-American psychoanalysis has looked to, and found, a different Freud. The Anglophone world has been partly misled by James Strachey, translator and editor of the Standard Edition. Strachey made key errors like "instinct" for Trieb, and "mind" for Seele. Worse by far, he thought Freud was talking about structures rather than processes. He introduced pseudo-medical Latin and terrible un-English abstractions like 'ideational', following Ernest Jones's instructions to make Freud appeal to scientists. Freud's own style was much more familiar.

While we agree with Chamberlain, we aim to develop a new model of the dreaming mind based on brain science. We hope this model may find acceptance in the humanities too, especially in art history, aesthetics, and art criticism.

AUTOCREATIVITY AND IMAGINATION IN REM SLEEP DREAMING

The characteristics of dreams that are of greatest interest to us are the formal properties of dreams that we have repeatedly emphasized throughout this book.

The vivid, internally generated perceptions of hallucinatory intensity which arise entirely spontaneously at regular, finite intervals during every night of sleep are a key point in our model. Instead of being merely visual these perceptions are strongly motoric. Instead of being regressive transformations of unacceptable drives, these perceptions are regarded as the undisguised read-out of the visuomotor brain. The dreamer is not simply beholding a scene, he is always an active protagonist in a scenario. If we were to liken this property to a single artistic medium it would be film. But dreaming is even more enveloping and engaging. It is more akin to virtual reality, because in that medium the subject's actions influence his or her perceptions. We consider the evidence to be overwhelmingly in favor of the idea that far from being regressive, or defensive, or in any way the guardian of sleep, the reliable, redundant, and recursive running of sensorimotor programs in dreaming sleep is itself autocreative because it constantly contributes to the development of our brains and our minds. This developmental dynamic is most critical in early fetal life but is still impressively active in early childhood. It is ongoing in middle age, when we might mistakenly have imagined development to be over. And even the aged remake themselves

Odilon Redon, Germination, 1879, Chicago Art Institute.

In his lithographs of dreams in an album with the title *Dans le rêve* (see also page 118) Redon shows dreaming as a germinal process in cosmogenic space. Redon was inspired by studies of the microscopic life in drops of pond water.

by refining the plastic connections of our brain-minds each night as they sleep.

The delusional conviction that these sensorimotor perceptions denote waking is a credit to the power of sleep to simulate the visuomotor experiences of the wake state. This fact shows that however bizarre may be the cognitive aspects of dreaming, we are using sleep to retain our performance skills and/or improve upon them. Dreaming is thus the subjective experience of a progressive program designed in a fail-safe manner to help us maintain and improve our behavioral repertoire. To the extent that modern artists like John Cage wanted to celebrate the aleatory over the predictable they were simulating REM sleep. We would like to stress that the Eastern meditative practices that are cultivated by artists like Cage are efforts to put the self and its art in the hands of a deeper, more reliable bearer of truth than human reason. These decisions all grant wisdom to physiology, the wisdom of the body as the Harvard physiologist, Walter Cannon, put it. It is not so much that we are demented in our dreams (though in a formal sense we are), as that we are surrendering one level of control (the cortical brain) to another (the subcortical brain). Both parts of the brain are important and each must have its day. In the case of the subcortical brain, its day is the night. The nocturnal niche is thus occupied by rest, by recovery, and by those reconstructive functions of the brain, mind, and body that are favored by darkness.

The incongruities and discontinuities of dream bizarreness are not induced by a censor to confuse hidden meanings but by an automatically programmed propensity to loosen some associations while tightening others. Humanistic critics have questioned our analogy of the bizarreness of the dreaming mind to delirium, the organic psychosis associated with brain dysfunction. We agree that no natural state can be pathological. We also insist that loosening some associations in favor of tight-ening others is very much what dream art is about. Indeed, the rules of association are so flagrantly loosened that sometimes dreams come up with tropes so brilliant as to rival art. At other times, however, the associative strain defies integration and there is a nervous (or mental) breakdown that can be reasonably likened to madness. Whichever path the dream takes, we want to emphasize our view that dreaming is bizarre for primarily physiological reasons. The chemical and regional organizers of logical cognition are asleep. They need to sleep not to safeguard consciousness, not to preserve sleep, and not to release what the ego has repressed, but to function optimally the next day.

Since the beginning of time, dream amnesia has been a source of frustration to those who would like to remember more of their nocturnal scenarios. Whether they are artists trying to garner ideas from their dreaming selves, dreamers hoping to gain insight into who they are, or anyone hoping to see a free film show in which he or she is the star, nature has made access to dreaming difficult. No artist would want his work to be so eminently forgettable as is the dream-maker's work in each of us. And yet, we get glimpses of our own creativity. Even without resorting to special dream harvesting techniques, we are likely to see enough to confirm the consistency of dream form and the informative accuracy of dream content. As sleepers we become dream authors, dream painters, dream acrobats, dream actors, and dream architects. We design Pointillist dream canvases that rival Seurat's. We perform on the high wire and tumble weightless as an astronaut in outer space. Bursting into flames, like the dreamer in Blake's engraving *Leonora's Dream*, we ride through infernal regions on a horse propelled by and spewing fire. And we build palaces of splendor never seen in the waking world. If we keep a dream journal we remember samples of what must be a vast treasure trove of dream

Dream Drawings.

Dreaming evokes fantastic images in all of us. We don't need to be artists to experience and represent such elaborate creations as the dream elevator, the dream bicycle, or the dream computer drawn by the Smithsonian Insect Specialist. Such images are not only innovative but also emotionally salient. This is particularly true of the desk top computer which enabled the dreamer to access his card file of insects and the bicycle which shows the bachelor-dreamer alone on a bicycle built for two.

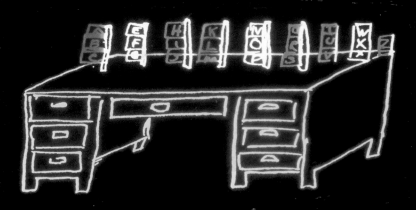

art. And if, like the Engine Man, we draw our dreams, we can even be reminded of the appearance of them again.

In order to account for the relative consistency and predictability of our thinking and behavior many people are naturally drawn to what might be called top-down models, such as creationism or cosmological design. We have taken the Christian angel, who brings God's messages to us in the form of dreams, to be the focal point of our dialectic about dreaming and art because it so clearly exemplifies this top-down kind of model. This model frees us from responsibility for our dreams, since we are simply conduits through which God's will is expressed.

Yet our lives and everything we know about them from biology suggest that as much and perhaps more can be explained by bottom-up rather than by top-down models. Bottom-up models not only acknowledge randomness, they celebrate it by showing that everything that characterizes top-down models, including rationality and creativity, depends upon it even as it undermines those precious faculties. The Darwinian model of evolution and the DNA model of molecular biology challenges creationism. The standard model of physics challenge cosmogenesis. The activation-synthesis model of dreaming likewise challenges all top-down models of dreaming.

What bottom-up models say is that simple elements, be they neurones, atomic particles, or ions behave randomly. They are little devils! When atomic particles collide, subparticles may be emitted and energy released. Ions do the same thing, but, being charged, they tend to line up. These energy releases and linings-up result, entirely by chance, in configurations which are durable, self-perpetuating, and even self-replicating. The only thing that is predictable in complex systems such as the human brain is the inevitable drift toward states of self-organization.

Neuronal Activity and Self Organization

Neurones, like the cells that constitute living plants and animals, are remarkable engines composed of self-replicating molecules of DNA packed into their nuclear chemical factory. Among the many talents of neurones is their capacity for storing the models of the world in memory. Since informational traffic moves both ways between the signal code system in the neuronal membrane and the neuronal nucleus, each signal causes a cascade of events that influences the state of the nuclear-chemical factory.

Neurones are cells with signal code-generating, receiving, and transmitting properties. One of the characteristics that neurones retain is the randomness from which they emerged. Although they do a very good job of representing and recording external reality, all of this encoding is abstract and imperfect. It is also subject to degradation according to the tendency of all neuronal systems to undergo spontaneous fluctuations in their level of activity and organization.

The interaction of neurones in the dreaming brain creates a system of self-organization which may give rise to order. Other systems in which self-organization has been shown to operate include the food foraging behavior of social insects, tumor growth in the immune system, urban evolution, and family system dynamics. In all of these examples, each element in the system has a deterministic life of its own. Through its interaction with its peers, it goes through dynamic phases which are characterized by an alternation of periods of chaotic disorder with periods of orderliness. The dreaming brain is a prime example of a self-organizing system.

Self-Organization and the Dreaming Brain

To understand self-organization in technical terms, let us compare the effects of heat on a pan of boiling water to the effects of activation on the state of the brain. As both systems are driven further from their initial equilibrium, they have a tendency to enter new states. In the case of water, the increasing convection causes the fluid to move from the bottom of the pan to the top and the system may reorganize into a pattern of hexagonally shaped cells, each of which is made up of millions of individual water molecules. In the case of the brain, as more and more neurons are recruited into a homogenous oscillation of increasing frequency and amplitude, the system can ultimately be driven to the boiling point of seizure generation. Seizure generation is abnormal but it is not irrelevant to our argument. Epileptic states, like dreams, have been considered to be of divine origin, to confer inspired visions, and even to contribute to creativity - as in the case of Fyodor Dostoyevsky who suffered from temporal lobe seizures. And REM sleep, with its PGO waves and temporal lobe activation, is a seizure-like normal state which evinces the phenomenon of self-organization in dreaming.

Dreamstage Mirror Wall.

At Harvard's Carpenter Center for the Visual Arts, we produced the exhibit called Dreamstage, An Experimental Portrait of the Sleeping Brain in 1977. A mirror wall separated the Dark Space (where sleep and its brain basis were demonstrated without explanation) from the Light Space (which contained artistic and didactic material about sleep and dream science). Under the curved mirror (which was conceived to reflect and distort the visitors image) was the EEG-photo sequence called the Allen Moore Scroll. (Photo by Josh Prokop).

The phenomenon of self-organization is a property of all non-linear systems, like the weather, boiling water, and the brain. The physicist David Kahn, who worked with Ilya Prigogine, the architect of self-organization theory, introduced us to these ideas and to the mathematical description of the qualitative change in systems that suddenly occurs when a critical threshold is exceeded. These sudden changes are called bifurcation points by linear stability analysts because they cause the system to acquire new properties. For example, when water is heated beyond a certain threshold it can no longer suppress the convective fluctuations that ultimately lead it to the boiling point. Then water becomes steam. When the brain is overactivated it cannot contain the convulsive discharges which lead to seizure. In general, when bifurcations lead to new stable states, they are a source of novelty in a system. In sleep, this is a regular occurrence.

Self-organization can be imagined as occurring at several levels in the brain during sleep. At one level we have the formation of relatively simple structures such as cortical columns or sets of columns in the visual cortex. Cortical columns are groups of thousands of vertically interconnected cells that function as units whenever we see an image or hallucinate. These very simple structures give rise, cognitively, to fragments of images which occur in non-REM sleep when cholinergic input from the brainstem is relatively low, but sufficient to maintain the brain far from equilibrium and allows self-organization to take place. More complex image formation self-organizes when additional bifurcations occur due to a further increase in cholinergic input to the disinhibited forebrain during the transition to REM sleep.

When PGO burst neurones begin to fire, even more complex image formation self-organizes as larger and larger areas of cortex are synchronously excited. Cognitively, these bursts may lead to dream bizarreness for two reasons. First, the PGO waves induce neuronal patterns which are incongruous with the ongoing dream narrative, but are nonetheless continuous with it. And second, the PGO waves, acting as environmental fluctuations, destabilize the existing neuronal organization causing new neuronal patterns to self-organize whose cognitive correlate may be a narrative discontinuity, such as dream characters who metamorphose into each other, or dream objects which follow one another in a loosely connected sequence.

At a still higher level, signals from the whole array of neuronal clusters comprising the rich cortical network, self-organize to produce dream narratives. For reasons that we will consider later, these narratives have a remarkable degree of stability. It interests us that this property could contribute to an overall coherence or "single mindedness" in dreams even in the presence of microscopic disorder. In all cases, self organization occurs because the neuronal system is non-linear and is maintained far from a state of equilibrium. For example, at the level of a single neurone, the neurone is not in equilibrium because of the sodium and potassium gradients across its membrane. The concentration of sodium is higher outside the cell than inside, and this difference is maintained by a sodium pump. Moreover, the concentration of potassium is higher inside than outside the cell.

It is important to be aware of the level of description being used in the definition of a system. At a more macroscopic level of description, say a neural network, the interest shifts from whether a single neurone is in equilibrium to whether the network is in equilibrium. For example, the neural network consisting of forebrain structures will be driven far from equilibrium if bombarded by signals from the brain stem. The distance from equilibrium is least when there is only aminergic disinhibition and greatest when there is

William Blake, *Leonora's Dream*, 1796. Collection Geoffrey Keynes, United Kingdom.

The engraving is the frontispiece to an English translation of the poem *Leonora* by Gottfried

Berger. The caption under the engraving begins with the lines: O! how I dreamt of things

impossible, / of Death affecting Forms least like himself.

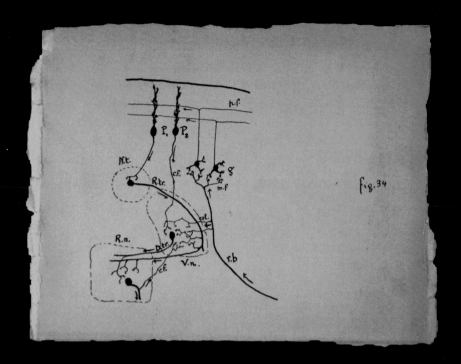

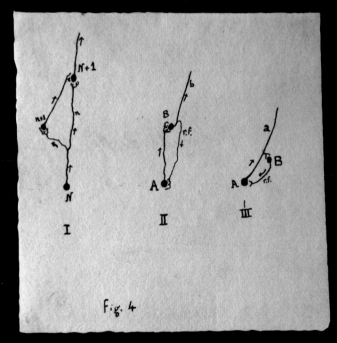

Drawings of Neuronal Circuits.

Raphael Lorente de Nò was one of Cajal's students and collaborators. Because he was an ear, nose, and throat specialist, he was particularly interested in the reflex movement of the eye in response to movement of the head. Two of his original drawings show the circuitry involved in this reflex and in mediating the continuous activity of neurones that must underlie consciousness.

cholinergic input and PGO waves. In the former case, neuronal self-organization would not occur very readily and hence dreaming is relatively rare without cholinergic input. This is because the ability of a system to self-organize is proportional to its distance from equilibrium, which in turn is related to the constraints acting upon the system. While sleeping, external input is mostly absent so that only the internally generated input is able to maintain the brain-mind system far from equilibrium.

Role of PGO Waves as Environmental Noise

In our model of the brain PGO waves appear to the cortical structures as environmental fluctuations. They are a neuronal activation factor akin to the convection of water molecules in the hot water analogy. In this role the PGO waves act as a noisy parameter and cause additional bifurcations which lead to additional self-organized images that add to the bizarreness of dream narratives. Since PGO waves occur predominantly during the REM sleep, it is not surprising that more vivid hallucinatory images would occur more frequently during that state than in the relatively noise free NREM environment.

In REM where the environment is noisy due to bursts of PGO spikes, new configurations of information develop as a result of processes called probability amplitude peak splitting, and shifted transition points. These two processes have their cognitive correlates, respectively, in the appearance of new images and in the appearance of displaced images. Dream narratives in REM thus contain more discontinuities, and more incongruities owing to the existence of the additional possible mathematical solutions brought about by the PGO noise.

It is well known that we often feel that our dreams just happen, and that as dreamers we exercise little control over our actions in the dream. This non-directed state is consistent with what occurs in other self-organizing systems. Even though self-organizing systems have external parameters that constrain their choices, the system itself nonetheless "decides" which of the many possible behaviors it will adopt. The choice is made through the fluctuations present within the system which push it to one or another stable state.

In the dreaming brain, the constraining forces come from internal memories, such as enduring records of conflict, desire, or concern, as well as more transitory traces of recent input, like the so-called day residues. But within these constraints, the fluctuations can lead to an extremely wide and highly unpredictable repertoire of possible combinations. There is thus a large chance for novelty and innovation in dreaming as fluctuations play with a seeming infinite supply of existing images and story lines. These features give the dreaming brain its extraordinary freedom. For us they constitute the very soul of art. And as in art, they make any system of reductionistic interpretations of content hazardous. According to activation-synthesis and self-organization, only the form of dreaming is predictable, not the content.

The Representation and Interpretation of Dreams

Neuroscience asserts that the creativity which Freud attributed to the unconscious mind in fact arises from the auto-activation of the brain. It now seems indisputable that all of us dream several times every night of our lives. While dreams are powerful presences, they pose and have throughout history posed the riddle of their origins: how and why they take the forms they do. It has always been recognized, as A. Alvarez has reminded us in his

Italian, c.a. 1290, The Dream of St. Francis, Upper Church of San Francesco, Assisi.

In this fresco the instructions to construct a church are transmitted to the dreaming saint by an angel. Today we would suggest that Saint Francis dreamt about building a church during REM sleep, and woke up with the design worked out by the autocreative mechanism of the dreaming brain during sleep. We have come a long way from ascribing even useful nocturnal visions to external agencies. Autocreativity is a natural function of our brains during sleep.

book *Night*, that only a fine line distinguishes dreams from madness:

Being mad means living in a closed, hallucinatory world so powerful that reality simply cannot get through, and that is precisely how the dreamer feels in the grip of his dream. But the dreamer wakes and is left with the irredeemable strangeness of what, in his dreams, had seemed perfectly rational.

And Alvarez poses the question of how we can account for the discontinuity between

the familiar world the waking dreamer opens his eyes to and the distorted, disoriented fantasy land of dreams, populated by strange and vivid presences, where time implodes and impossible events seem perfectly normal.

Whatever the answer to this question may be, the agent that bridges the realms of waking and dreaming is art. The problem is that both art and dreaming ultimately resist interpretation. At the turn of the fifth century, Synsius of Cyrene said in *De Insomniis* (Concerning Dreams):

In dreams one conquers, walks, or flies simultaneously, and the imagination has room for it all; but how shall mere speech find room for it?

Erik Erikson acknowledged as much when he wrote:

One has never seen anybody else's dream nor has the slightest proof that it ever "happened" the way one visualizes it. The report of a dream, in turn, arouses in each listener and interpreter a different set of images, which are as incommunicable as is the dream itself.

Given these caveats, it is surprising that more caution has not been exercised in the interpretation of dreams. We do not anticipate that many readers will share our emphasis on the fundamental uninterpretability of dreaming and art. We hope, however, that they will understand the costs and benefits of the two models that complete with each other.

In what we will call the standard model of 20th-century interpretability, mental content and form are both reducible to historical antecedents, whether those antecedents be personal, historical, or situational. This is the model of psychoanalysis, of hermeneutics, and contextual studies. In what we will call the new scientific brain/mind model, historical antecedence is given an important role in shaping content, but has little to do with the form of mental processes except in so far as biological history has brought our brain/minds to their capacity for self-organization. The first model is willing to give up freedom for the comfort of interpretability. It prefers angels to neurones. The second model gives up the comfort of interpretability for the freedom of creativity. It prefers neurones to angels.

As we conclude our book, it is fitting that we take up once more the issue of interpretation, focusing on dreaming, but extending it to art and science more generally. Contextually oriented humanists like to insist that every act of mind, including every scientific formulation, is so bound up in topicality, locality, economics, and social structure as to doom to hopeless relativism any theory of causation. We understand and accept these cautions, as far as they go, but we think that they do not go far enough, for they do not address the issue of scientific falsifiability which seems to us to be the ultimate test of any theory, and the only one that could free a theory from the argument of cultural relativism. To help us develop this line of thought we cite the Portuguese literary critic Miguel Tamen to the effect that "interpretation, minimally defined, [is] the attribution of language and intention."

It is a given that all dream reports or analyses are interpretations. Objections to the interpretation of dreams are not to interpretation as such. Rather, they are objections, as Tamen has pointed out, to certain specific interpretations. Let us consider this dream report:

In my dream I looked down on a new line of fence postholes dug by my northerly neighbor, and I was surprised to see that he had moved them two feet in his directions.

The dreamer himself, wishing to make the point that his dream report - not, we should emphasize, the dream as dreamt - does not lend itself and does not require interpretation, has commented on it as follows:

The net effect of this supremely generous neighbourly act was a gift of about 200 square feet of valuable real estate. A theory of consciousness that emphasizes desire has little problem with the particular content of this particular conscious experience. I am territorial. My dream reveals it. But besides being disappointedly uninformative - since I am already quite conscious of my territoriality - the desire paradigm leaves unsolved - and even untouched - the completely autocreative aspect of my conscious experience while dreaming.

Yet the assertions that digging the new line of fence posts is a "supremely generous neighbourly act," that the dream reveals the dreamer's "territoriality," that the new line of fence posts "was a gift of about 200 square feet of valuable real estate," and that the dream corresponds to "a theory of consciousness that emphasizes desire" are, of course, all acts of interpretation. As such, they are objectively undemonstrable, and could be replaced by four other equally undemonstrable assertions (or interpretations).

We agree with Tamen that these interpretations are gratuitous and arbitrary. In fact, we introduced them to suggest that this approach to dream theory building is scientifically untenable. This dream report - and its interpretation - are in fact a parody of Freud and of the hermeneuticist in all of us. The main point is that not just this dream, but all dreams, are autocreative. If it can be objectively demonstrated that the brain/mind will generate this kind of confabulatory scenario whenever it is activated in a certain way, but that its content is unpredictable, then the formal aspects of our dream theory are validated and our skepticism about the validity of any content-oriented theory is reciprocally strengthened.

In our view, dream content interpretation is not entirely off limits to science. Once the formal aspects of dreaming are adequately dealt with, then - and only then – is content ready for rigorous analysis. And we would certainly not rule out a scientific reduction of intention to emotional drives like fear and anxiety or joy and elation. These brain-based intentional states would in fact appear to us to operate causally in the shaping of the content of both dreams and art.

We recognize that making our model work demands guidelines for the maintenance and exploitation of the creative potential of the brain/mind which are practical, easily understood, and fruitful. To solidify our position, we return to Tamen, who has written that

Complaints about interpretation are not different than complaints about the law of gravity. Interpretation is no less than the very form of all possible descriptions, and complaints about interpretation are simply complaints about certain interpretations. Whenever one does suggest there is no necessity to interpretation, one is really only reacting against certain interpretations.

Interpretation, Tamen has also suggested, essentially boils down to what he has called "proper description."

We like Tamen's reference to the law of gravity, which for a hundred years has successfully served the exploration of space first with optical telescopes, then with radio telescopes, and, in our lifetime, with manned and unmanned vehicle probes. And it is well to remember that Galileo is admired not only as a scientist, but also for his courage in taking on one of the most powerful and self-serving of all hermeneutic institutions, the Catholic church. We also like Tamen's gravitation example because it allows us to emphasize our point about inner space, cerebral space, the space which has suffered so long at the hands of animistic model builders with respect to its causal mechanisms, and of hermeneutic textualists regarding its verbal and schematic products.

The fact is that brain science is now at the same level of development as astronomy when Galileo observed that the movements of the celestial bodies were seen to obey natural laws. The universe was self-organized. And, entirely by chance, one planet, called Earth, had fallen into an orbit at just the right distance from the sun to make its atmosphere and the evolution of life up to and including human consciousness possible.

What is the neurobiological equivalent of the law of gravity? Certainly not the neurone doctrine, which is more like Galileo's description of the moons around Jupiter than the theory of gravity. We suggest that the brain's own gravitational law is inherent in the cerebral mechanism which guarantees the internal, dynamic state changes that generate the NREM-REM sleep cycle. The brain thus continually reconstructs itself updating its memory and integrating the emotional valence attached to its many elements. The autocreative brain-mind spins off its sometimes foolish, sometimes sensible, and occasionally sublime mental products, those models of the world and of consciousness itself that we call art and science.

Bibliography

Bibliography

- W. Abel, *The Collective Dream in Art*, New York, 1966.
- V. Adolphs, "Monstren der Einbildungskraft. Goyas Caprichos und andere Träume der Vernunft", *Die Erfindung der Natur*, Freiburg-im-Breisgau, 1994, 80-99.
- S. Alexandrian, *Le Surrealisme et le rêve*, Paris, 1974.
- A. Alvarez, *Night*, New York, 1995.
- J.S. Antrobus, "Dreaming: Cognitive processes during cortical activation and high afferent thresholds". *Psychological Review*, 1991, 98:96-121.
- Artemidorus, *The Interpretation of Dreams*, trans. R.J. White, Park Ridge, 1975.
- E. Aserinsky and N. Kleitman, "Regularly Occurring Periods of Eye Mobility and Concomitant Phenomena During Sleep", *Science*, 118, 1953, 273-74.
- G. Bachelard, *The Poetic Reverie*, trans. D. Russell, Boston, 1971.
- A. Béguin, *L'âme romantique et le rêve*, Paris, 1939.
- W. Born, "A History of Dream Interpretation", *The Dream. CIBA Symposia*, 10/2, 1948, 926-39.
- W. Born, "The Dream and Art", *The Dream. CIBA Symposia*, 10/2, 1948, 940-51.
- G. Cardano, *Sul sonno e sul sognare*, ed. M. Mancia and A. Grieco, Venice, 1989.
- P. Castelli, "La natura del sogno", *Uomo e natura nella letteratura e nell'arte italiana del tre-quattrocento*, ed. W. Prinz, Florence, 1988, 201-25.
- S. Coellier, "Les rêves illustré de J.J. Grandville (1803-1847)", *Revue de l'art*, 92, 1991, 51-63.
- A. Dahlstrom and K. Fuxe, "Evidence for the existence of monoamine-containing neurons in the central nervous system. I. Demonstration in the cell bodies of brain stem neurons", *Acta Physiologica Scandinavica*, 1964, 62:1-55.
- W. Dement and N. Kleitman, "The relation of eye movements during sleep to dream activity: An objective method for the study of dreaming", *Journal of Experimental Psychology*, 1957, 53:339-46.
- C. Dempsey, *Inventing the Renaissance Putto*, Chapel Hill and London, 2001.
- E.V. Evarts, "Activity of neurons in visual cortex of the cat during sleep with low voltage fast EEG activity", *Journal of Neurophysiology*, 1962, 25: 812-16.
- D. Foulkes, *The psychology of sleep*, 1966, Charles Scribner's Sons.
- H. Focillon, *I disegni di Victor Hugo*, Bologna, 1983.
- J. Ford, *Coleridge on Dreaming*, Cambridge, 1998.
- S. Freud, Project for a Scientific Psychology. In: *The Origins of Psychoanalysis. Letters to Wilhelm Fleiss, Drafts and Notes: 1887-1902*, 1895, ed. M. Bonaparte, A. Freud & E. Kris. Basic Books.
- S. Freud, *The Interpretation of Dreams*, trans. J. Strachey, London, 1953.
- F. Gandolfo, *Il "dolce tempo": mistica, ermetismo e sogno nel cinquecento*, Rome, 1978.
- J. Gardner, "Papal Dreams and Painted Palaces: An Essay in Mediaeval Oneiric Iconography", *Träume im Mittelalter*, ed. A. Paravicin and G. Stabile, Stuttgart, 1989.
- W. Gibson, "Bosch's Dreams: A Reponse to the Art of Bosch in the Sixteenth Century", *The Art Bulletin*, 74, 1992, 205-17.
- R. Goldwater, *Space and Dream*, New York, 1967.
- G.F. Hartlaub, "Albrecht Dürers Aberglaube", *Zeitschrift für Kunstwissenschaft*, 7/2, 1953.
- J.A. Hobson, *The Dreaming Brain*, New York, 1988.
- J.A. Hobson, *Sleep*, Scientific American Library, 1989.
- J.A. Hobson, *Consciousness*, Scientific American Library, 1999.
- J.A. Hobson, *Dreaming as delirium*, Cambridge, MA: The MIT Press, 1999.
- J.A. Hobson, *The dream drug store*, Cambridge, MA: MIT Press, 2001.
- J.A. Hobson, *Dreaming: an introduction to the science of sleep*, Oxford: Oxford University Press, 2002.
- J.A. Hobson, *13 dreams Freud never had : the new mind science*, Pi Press, 2004.
- J.A. Hobson and J.A. Leonard, *Out of its mind: psychiatry in crisis*, Cambridge, MA: Perseus Publishing, 2001.
- J.A. Hobson, R.W. McCarley, P.W. Wyzinski, "Sleep cycle oscillation: reciprocal discharge by two brainstem neuronal groups", *Science*, 1975 189:55-8.
- J.A. Hobson and R.W. McCarley, "The Brain as a Dream State Generator: An Activation-Synthesis Hypothesis of the Dream Process", *American Journal of Psychiatry*, 134/12, 1977, 1335-48.
- J.A. Hobson and E.F. Pace-Schott, "The Cognitive Neuroscience of Sleep: Neuronal Systems, Consciousness and Learning". *Nature Reviews Neuroscience*, 2002, 3:679-693.

- J.A. Hobson, E.F. Pace-Schott, and R. Stickgold, "Dreaming and the brain: Toward a cognitive neuroscience of conscious states", *Behavioral and Brain Sciences*, 2000, 23:793-842.
- J.A. Hobson, R. Stickgold and E.P. Pace-Scott, "The Neuropsychology of REM Sleep Dreaming", *Neuroreport*, 9, 1998, R1-R14.
- A.L. Hodgkin, and A.F. Huxley, "Currents carried by sodium and potassium ions through the membrane of the giant axon of Loligo", *J. Physiol.*, 1952, 116:449-72.
- W. Hofmann, *Johan Tobias Sergel, 1740-1814*, Munich, 1975.
- J. Hundt, *Der Traumglaube bei Homer*, Greifswald, 1935.
- T. James, *Dreams, Creativity and Madness in Nineteenth-Century* France, Oxford, 1995.
- W. James, *The principles of psychology.* Dover, 1890.
- W. James, *Varieties of religious experience.* New York: Touchstone, 1902.
- M. Jouvet, "Recherche sur les structures nerveuses et les mechanismes responsables des differentes phases du sommeil physiologique", *Archives Italiennes de Biologie*, 1962, 100:125-206.
- M. Jouvet, *Le sommeil et le rêve*, Paris, 1992.
- M. Jouvet and F. Michel, "Correlation electromyographiques du sommeil chez le chat decortique et mesencephalique chronique", *C.R. Soc. Biol.*, 1959, 153:422-25.
- D. Kahn and J.A. Hobson, "Self-organization theory of dreaming". *Dreaming*, 1993, 3:151-78.
- D.B. Klein, *The Unconscious: Invention or Discovery? A Historiocritical Inquiry*, Santa Monica, 1977.
- B.L. Knapp, *Dream and Image*, Troy (NY), 1977.
- J.L. Koerner, "Bosch's Equipment", *Things That Talk*, ed. L. Daston, New York, 2004.
- P. Lavie and J.A. Hobson, "Origin of Dreams: Anticipation of Modern Dream Theories in the Philosophy and Physiology of the Eighteenth and Nineteenth Centuries", *Psychological Bulletin*, 100, 1986, 229-40.
- Macrobius, *Commentary on the Dream of Scipio*, trans. W.H. Stahl, New York, 1952.
- J. Maritain, *The Dream of Descartes*, New York, 1944.
- A. Maury, "Du sommeil et du somnaubolisme au point de vue psychologique", *Le Revue des Deux Mondes*, 14, 1858, 927-49.
- R.W. McCarley and J.A. Hobson, "Neuronal excitability modulation over the sleep cycle: A structural and mathematical model", *Science*, 1975, 189:58-60.
- R.W. McCarley and J.A. Hobson, "The Forms of Dreams and the Biology of Sleep", *Handbook of Dreams*, ed. B.B. Wolman, New York, 1979, 76-130.
- R.W. McCarley and J.A. Hobson, "The Neurobiological Origins of Psychoanalytic Dream Theory", *The American Journal of Psychiatry*, 134, 1977, 1211-21.
- A. Mellerio, *Odilon Redon. Peintre, Dessinateur et Graveur*, Paris, 1923.
- F. Meyer, "Traum und bildende Kunst", *Träum and Traumen*, ed. T. Wagner-Simon and G. Benedetti, Göttingen, 1984, 162-78.
- G. Moruzzi and H.W. Magoun, "Brainstem reticular formation and activation of the EEG". *Electroencephalography and Clinical Neurophysiology*, 1949 1:455-73.
- T.A. Nielsen, "Mentation in REM and NREM sleep: A review and possible reconciliation of two models", *Behavioral and Brain Sciences*, 2000, 23:851-66.
- H.J. Norman, "William Blake", *The Journal of Mental Science*, 61, 1915, 198-244.
- E.F. Pace-Schott and J.A. Hobson, "The Neurobiology of Sleep: Genetic Mechanisms, Cellular Neurophysiology and Subcortical Networks", *Nature Reviews Neuroscience*, 2002, 3:591-605.
- E. Panofsky, "Zwei Dürerprobleme", *Münchner Jahrbuch der bildenden Kunst*, N.F. 8, 1931, 1-48.
- V. Petric, ed., *Film and Dreams. An Approach to Bergman*, South Salem (NY), 1981.
- D. Pick and L. Roper, eds., *Dreams and History*, London and New York, 2004.
- M. Polizzotti, *Revolution of the Mind. The Life of André Breton*, New York, 1995.
- N. Powell, *Fuseli: The Nightmare*, London, 1973.
- G. Radetti, "Demoni e sogni nella critica di Callimaco Esperiente al Ficino", *Umanesimo e esoterismo*, ed. E. Castelli, Padua, 1960, 117-21.
- C. Sala, *Max Ernst et la démarche onirique*, Paris, 1970.
- J.P. Sartre, *The Psychology of Imagination*, New York, 1948.
- A. Schopenhauer, *Parerga und Paralipomena*, Berlin, 1857.
- A. Schwarz, *Man Ray*, London, 1977.
- P.A. Sitney, *Visionary Film. The American Avant-Garde*, New York, 1974.
- J.T. Soby, *Giorgio de Chirico*, New York, 1955.
- J.T. Soby, *René Magritte*, New York, 1965.
- B.O. States, *Seeing in the Dark: Reflections on Dreams and Dreaming*, New Haven and London, 1997.
- L. Steinberg, "Picasso's Sleep Watchers", *Other Criteria*, London, 1972, 93-114.
- R. Stickgold, J.A. Hobson, R. Fosse and M. Fosse, "Sleep, Learning and Dreams: Off-line memory reprocessing", *Science*, 2001, 294, 1052-1057.
- D. Sylvester, *About Modern Art*, London, 1996.
- M. Tamen, *Friends of Interpretable Objects*, Cambridge (MA) and London, 2001.
- *Victor Willing: A Retrospective Exhibition 1952-1985*, London, 1986.
- J.D. Watson and F.H.C.Crick, "Molecular Structure of Nucleic Acids. I. A Structure for Deoxyribose Nucleic Acid", *Nature*, 1953, 171:737-38.
- L. Whyte, *The Unconscious Before Freud*, New York, 1978.
- L. Williams, *Figures of Desire. A Theory and Analysis of Surrealist Film*, Urbana, Chicago and London, 1981.
- F.A. Wolf, *The dreaming universe: a mind-expanding journey into the realm where psyche and physics meet*, New York: Touchstone, 1995.

CREDITS

April 2005
Printed in Italy